MACDONALD TRENDS AND DEVELOPMENTS
IN ENGINEERING SERIES

General Editor Sir Willis Jackson, F.R.S.

Professor of Electrical Engineering
Imperial College of Science and Technology

20

A GUIDE TO THE LASER

A Guide to the Laser

Edited by
DAVID FISHLOCK

AMERICAN ELSEVIER PUBLISHING COMPANY, INC.
NEW YORK

© MACDONALD & CO. (PUBLISHERS) LTD., 1967

First published 1967

AMERICAN ELSEVIER PUBLISHING COMPANY, INC.

52 Vanderbilt Avenue,

New York, New York 10017

LIBRARY OF CONGRESS CATALOG NUMBER 67-22189

Printed in Great Britain

CONTENTS

INTRODUCTION

DAVID FISHLOCK
'New Scientist', *London*

On the door of a laboratory in California is a picture from a popular magazine, of a light beam blasting a missile from the sky, boldly titled THE INCREDIBLE LASER. A second legend has been added: 'For credible lasers see inside'. That defaced picture neatly summarizes the brief history of the laser, one of the most exciting discoveries of modern physics: a source of energy with properties quite different from anything known before. For astonishing though the properties of laser light must appear — in its capacity to drill through a diamond or convey a cluster of television programmes, take three-dimensional photographs or illuminate a distant scene — they still scarcely match the flights of fancy of journalists, or even the hopes and fears of military men.

It is the first purpose of this book to provide those who might make use of the laser with authoritative accounts of the invention, its several forms, and their properties, and to indicate the most promising lines of progress with its application. This has been done before, in several books, although the books which have appeared during the seven years since the laser first was demonstrated have tended inevitably to grow rapidly out of date in their discussion of applications. But a second, perhaps more important purpose of this book is to stimulate its readers to explore and discover their own applications for 'coherent light', the laser's curious radiation.

Ten British scientists, all of whom have made contributions to the science and technology of lasers, have set down their views on an invention first proposed in 1958 and first demonstrated in 1960, yet already known by reputation to millions for its (incredible) parts in cinema and television films. The eleventh contributor is an American technical journalist, and his contribution on the uses of the laser in warfare (Chapter 6) in many respects is the most exciting.

'Fall-out', the incidental benefits that can accrue from big projects, especially military ones, that advance the frontiers of a technology, has occasioned much debate in the last two or three years, as the exponential rise of military research budgets soared to astronomical figures. It can be argued that almost the entire technology of the laser, which by 1965 was costing an estimated $60 million in the USA alone, is 'fall-out' from a concept the possibilities of which the military had already recognized before the first demonstration in the spring of 1960. It is for this reason that I have chosen to discuss the military applications of the laser before those of civilian science and technology.

But to say this is not to underestimate scientific interest in the laser, which has been immense — and not simply because the device soon turned out to be one easily and inexpensively obtained, by the standards of modern physics. It has been immense because the laser emits a kind of light found neither in nature nor in any previous source of electromagnetic radiation: light of unrivalled 'purity' and intensity. An important part of this scientific interest, motivated still in large measure by military thinking, has been to see how far the laser might 'stretch' — in one direction to lower, in the other to higher frequencies. In a field plainly dominated by American research, a British laboratory made a notable contribution in stretching the laser to a wavelength of 337 microns, potentially a most valuable wavelength (see Chapter 9); while other valuable contributions have been made in Russian and French laboratories.

Less than seven years after its invention the laser is already a practical tool in several different ways. Whether in the long run it will prove competitive in these roles must depend on a complex of factors. For example, as a welding tool (see Chapter 7) the laser will be in competition with the electron-beam welder, which enjoys an important tactical advantage in having been developed first. Even so, the laser can offer four distinct advantages: it generates no X-rays, it needs no vacuum, its beam is easier to focus with great precision, and because there is less heat lost by conduction it can be faster. Again, in communications the laser must compete highly with developed 'conventional' lines of communication, established at great expense, but this has not prevented Russian telecommunications engineers from installing a three-mile laser telephone 'cable' in Moscow, from the University on Lenin Hills to Zubovskaya Square telephone exchange, where it joins an automatic telephone system.

Two examples discussed at length, holography (Chapters 2 and 5) and ophthalmology (Chapter 8), are of applications for which the laser appears unrivalled. Professor Gabor's early work on holograms, or diffraction patterns, in the 1940s was hampered by lack of a sufficiently powerful source of coherent light. This the laser can supply. Of the many fascinating possibilities for holograms, none holds greater promise than as a tool for scientific research. The computer has given the scientist a remarkably powerful tool for analysing immense quantities of data, and to match its abilities and exploit its power to the full the scientist needs simple systems for gathering very large amounts of data at minimum inconvenience to himself. Holography promises to provide one such system: a simple means for gathering data that can then be analysed by a complex system. One possibility is its use to analyse patterns of vibrations and stresses too complex to unravel by other means. Holography may yet emerge as the most important laser technique of all.

In contrast, as the author of Chapter 8 points out, one reason why the laser has found early success in medical experiments is probably that it was applied to specific problems, while elsewhere there was a tendency to regard the new device as 'a solution in search of a problem' and to try and apply it on a too broad a front, almost inevitably with many disappointments. There are lessons in each of these examples for those who would apply the laser to other problems.

It is but a short step from medical applications to personal hazards. Men for decades have dreamed of a ray that might be 'fired'—to kill an adversary, perhaps, or knock out an engine. The laser hardly fulfils this dream, for the rapidly growing power of even this remarkable instrument is small unless focused by a lens placed very close to the target. Unfortunately such a lens exists in man's eyes.

I once visited a laboratory where they had put laser light 'on tap', by rigging a helium-neon laser and simply using mirrors to tap off the radiation as required elsewhere in the room. I would guess that they have abandoned this ingenious scheme since gas lasers of much higher power, such as the carbon dioxide and the argon lasers, made their appearance. But even with the milliwatt power levels of the early gas lasers it was a dangerous practice to have coherent radiation flashing indiscriminately around the room. With the power levels now obtainable from ruby and other pulsed lasers, this hazard can be considerable, and cases of permanent blindness have been recorded following a direct hit of a pulse of laser light on the eyeball.

I am naturally extremely grateful to the eleven contributors whose collaboration has made this book possible, but I would also record my thanks to the editor of *New Scientist* for his permission to reproduce Chapter 5, most of which was originally commissioned from Professor Gabor as an article for that magazine. Part of Chapter 2 has also appeared in *New Scientist*.

1

THE BIRTH OF THE LASER

DR J. H. SANDERS

Clarendon Laboratory, Oxford

In the issue of the *Physical Review* for 1st July 1954 appeared a short announcement by J. P. Gordon, H. J. Zeiger and C. H. Townes which began 'An experimental device, which can be used as a very high resolution spectrometer, a microwave amplifier, or a very stable oscillator, has been built and operated'.[1] The device soon came to be known as the maser; in the form described, it operated in the microwave region of the spectrum, at a wavelength close to 1.25 cm.

This was the first news of a generator of electromagnetic radiation based on the phenomenon of 'stimulated emission'. Some six years later, Maiman produced the first laser, a stimulated-emission generator of radiation in the visible and infrared regions. Although the maser and the laser are based on exactly the same principles their properties are in many ways quite different.

The maser, whose name comes from 'Microwave Amplification by Stimulated Emission of Radiation', is a low-noise amplifier of microwaves, and in this form has been used, for example, in receivers for satellite communication links. It is also a generator of a very stable frequency and, since this frequency is essentially determined by the energy difference between a pair of energy levels in an atom or molecule, it can also be used as a fundamental standard of frequency or time.

The laser, on the other hand, is of little interest as an amplifier, and is not basically useful as a standard of wavelength in the optical region. It has outstanding properties in its various forms as a generator of both time coherent and spatially coherent radiation; these properties lead to the very narrow spectral width and directionality of its output. It is also a generator of unprecedented power in the visible and infrared. Unlike its predecessor, the maser, the laser is a very simple device to build and to operate.

The maser principle
The development of the maser and the laser came about by a series of

logical steps; these brought together knowledge from both theoretical and experimental fields. The idea that atoms could exist in discrete energy states, and could radiate light of well-defined frequencies in transitions between these energy states, was first proposed by Bohr in 1913 in his theory of the hydrogen atom. The process is shown diagrammatically in Fig. 1.

Bohr successfully accounted quantitatively for the main features of the spectrum of hydrogen and similar atoms, and produced good agreement with the results of spectroscopic work which had reached a very high degree of precision in the preceding decades. Bohr's theory dealt with the line spectrum of atoms observed in emission and in absorption, Fig. 1(a) and (b), which correspond respectively to a release of energy ΔE from the atom in the form of electromagnetic radiation of frequency ν, and to an absorption of the same amount of energy from a electromagnetic wave of frequency ν. The energy and the frequency are related by $\Delta E = h\nu$, where h is Planck's constant.

In 1917, Einstein, in the course of a theoretical investigation of black-body radiation, showed that the existence of a third process was necessary to account for the observed form of the spectrum of black-body radiation. This was stimulated emission of radiation. It is the converse of absorption, but is distinct from the process of spontaneous emission.

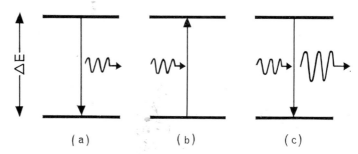

Figure 1 Diagrammatic representation of the processes of (*a*) spontaneous emission, (*b*) absorption, and (*c*) stimulated emission, between two energy levels.

An atom in the upper energy state shown in Fig. 1(a), even when completely isolated from any external influences, eventually spontaneously falls to the lower energy state and emits radiation. If one considers a randomly-orientated set of atoms, the spontaneous emission from them is equal in all directions; moreover the individual wave trains are emitted from the atoms at random times.

The time coherence of such radiation is limited by the length of each wave train emitted by the atoms, typically between 10^{-9} and 10^{-7}

second (1–100 nanoseconds). A source which consists of a number of excited atoms emitting spontaneously, such as the familiar discharge lamp, is spatially incoherent, since there is a random relationship between the waves emitted from various parts of the source.

Stimulated emission takes place when electromagnetic radiation of frequency ν, which corresponds to the energy change ΔE, falls on an atom in the upper energy state, Fig. 1(c). The atom is then stimulated to radiate by the presence of the radiation; this process competes with spontaneous emission, and an atom in an electromagnetic field may emit either by spontaneous emission or by stimulated emission. The relative probabilities can readily be calculated, and the results show that in all conventional atomic light sources, such as discharge lamps, the amount of stimulated emission is quite negligible. For this reason the subject of stimulated emission was for many years virtually ignored.

When stimulated radiation is emitted from an atom the energy which is released is added to that of the wave which stimulates it. The original wave is thus amplified, and the coherence of the original wave is preserved. This process is fundamental to the maser principle.

The first half of the twentieth century brought a steady development of the field of electronics and the extension of available sources of radiation in the radio-frequency region (see Fig. 2). The triode

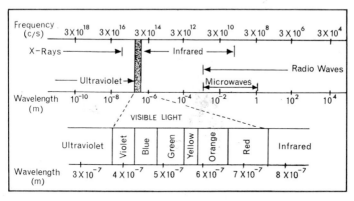

Figure 2   Sketch of the electromagnetic spectrum.

provided continuous coherent oscillation at frequencies which, by the outbreak of the Second World War, had extended gradually up to a few hundred megacycles per second. During the war the demands of radar brought about rapid development of the klystron, and the invention of the cavity magnetron, which made available frequencies up to the region of 50,000 Mc/s (a wavelength of 6 mm). Even today the frequency available from an electronic oscillator of this sort is only a little higher, for the simple reason that the device has become so small that it becomes difficult to obtain an electron beam current through it sufficiently large to maintain oscillation. Powers of about 10 milliwatts have been produced at wavelengths in the region of 0.7 mm, and lower-power oscillation has been observed at wavelengths as short as 0.38 mm. New developments in this field are in the laboratory stage and seem promising for the generation of power in the region of 0.1 mm, but would require the use of magnetic fields of several hundred kilogauss.

During the whole of this period of nearly half a century there was no fundamental development of sources of radiation in the visible and infrared regions. For most spectroscopic purposes adequately intense sources were available in the visible and near-infrared, but between that region and the microwave region lay a gap where a hot body gives very little radiation and detectors are comparatively insensitive, so that high-resolution spectroscopy is not possible. Then about 1950 interest began to develop in possible ways to generate radiation by a new technique, and preferably one which could be used to produce powerful sources in the region between microwaves and the infrared.

The theory of absorption and stimulated emission shows that, when an atom or molecule with two energy levels is placed in an electromagnetic field, the probability of an upward transition from the lower state — that is, absorption — Fig. 1(b) is, weighting factors apart, equal to the probability of a downward transition from the upper state — that is, stimulated emission, Fig. 1(c).

In the published literature there are occasional references to the 'negative absorption' which would occur if there were a predominance of atoms or molecules in the upper state, so that stimulated emission occurred at a greater rate than absorption. V. I. Fabrikant, in 1939, published his doctorate thesis at the Lebedev Institute in Moscow and briefly discussed negative absorption, as did Lamb and Retherford in 1950 in a footnote to a paper on the measurement of the 'Lamb shift' in hydrogen. There was probably a good deal of unpublished thought along these lines during this period, such as that which Houtermans mentions in a paper published in 1960, where he states that he had considered in the 1930s the possibility of amplification of radiation by such a process.

The ammonia maser

The years 1951 and 1952 saw independent progress by a number of people towards a concrete suggestion for the device which came to be known as a maser. Among these were Townes, then at Columbia University, New York, and Basov and Prokhorov of the Lebedev

Institute in Moscow; these three men (Fig. 3) were later to share the 1964 Nobel Prize for Physics for their work.

It appears that, for a time, one stumbling block was the view that no source of radiation could give a greater spectral intensity than that of a black body. This argument applies, however, only under conditions of thermal equilibrium; if equilibrium is disturbed the restriction no longer applies. Townes states that in the spring of 1951 the idea for a device for using amplification by stimulated emission

Figure 3 Left to right J. P. Gordon, N. G. Basov, H. J. Zeiger, A. M. Prokhorov and C. H. Townes, at the First Quantum Electronics Conference, Bloomingbury, NY, 1959. (*Photograph, courtesy J. H. Sanders.*)

came to him while he was sitting in Franklin Park, Washington, D.C., admiring the azalea blossoms.

Equilibrium could be disturbed in a beam of molecules, he conjectured, so as to produce a predominance of the molecules in the upper of two energy levels. The molecules could then be passed into a cavity tuned to the frequency of the transition between the energy levels. Here the molecules would be stimulated to emit their energy by a signal passed into the cavity, and the signal would thus be amplified.

If the number of molecules were large enough, the radiation in the cavity might be maintained at a level where the cavity's losses were compensated by the energy from the molecules, so that the device would oscillate continuously. In the microwave region the rate of spontaneous emission is very low, and introduces no problem, as it does in the optical region. Townes has described how he quickly worked out the conditions on the back of an envelope. Later that year the proposals were announced at a Symposium on Sub-millimeter Waves at the University of Illinois.

Subsequent work at Columbia University by Townes and his two research students, Gordon and Zeiger, culminated in the successful operation of a maser using ammonia molecules late in 1953. Meanwhile, at an All-Union Conference on Radio-Spectroscopy in May

Figure 4 Early maser amplifier being assembled at Mullard Research Laboratories for the GPO's satellite communications receiving station at Goonhilly.

1952, Basov and Prokhorov pointed out the theoretical possibility of constructing a 'molecular generator' of this type; and in 1954 they published the theory of a beam-type device very similar to that of Townes. Among others who published proposals of a similar nature at about this time was Weber of the University of Maryland. Russian work resulted in the operation of an ammonia maser in late 1955 or early 1956, although by that time they had published full theoretical accounts of the maser in which full credit is given to the work of Townes.

Extending the maser

Once the feasibility of the working maser had been demonstrated a number of research teams entered the field, and one major advance which resulted was the development of the three-level solid-state maser, which had the advantage over the molecular beam type in that it is tunable instead of being restricted to a single, fixed frequency. One version of the solid-state maser uses Zeeman (magnetically split) levels in the ground state of the chromium ions in a ruby crystal, and it is this form which is used as a low-noise amplifier in satellite communications (Fig. 4). It should be noted that one form of the laser also uses a ruby crystal, but the energy levels involved are quite different from those used in the microwave maser.

Although much thought was devoted to the operation of beam-type masers at frequencies higher than the microwave region, no feasible design was proposed; the difficulty was mainly the increased beam density required at a higher operating frequency. Plainly a new approach was needed.

It was realized that a maser-type oscillator has two essentials. One is an amplifying medium (atoms, molecules or ions) having a greater population density in the upper of two energy levels than in the lower. The second is a resonant cavity, in which the amplifying medium is placed.

The amplification of the radiation on passing through the amplifying medium must be large enough to overcome the inevitable losses in the cavity, so that oscillations are sustained. The amplifying medium is often referred to as having an 'inverted population' or being in a state of 'negative temperature'. This arises from the application to this state of affairs of the Boltzmann relation, which states that, in thermal equilibrium, the ratio of the upper-state population to the lower-state population is:

$$\exp - (\Delta E/kT)$$

where k is Boltzmann's constant and T is the absolute temperature. An inverted population is clearly not an equilibrium state, but if the Boltzmann relation is applied (or rather mis-applied) a negative value of the temperature is deduced. In the design of a maser some means must be found of disturbing thermal equilibrium so as to produce an adequate inversion of population.

First proposals for the optical maser

In the December 1958 issue of the *Physical Review* appeared a lengthy paper by Townes and his brother-in-law, Dr Arthur Schawlow.[2] At that time Townes was Professor at Columbia University and Schawlow was at the nearby Bell Telephone Laboratories at Murray Hill, New Jersey. The two had previously frequently collaborated; they were, for example, co-authors of a large volume on microwave spectroscopy.

In the *Physical Review* paper, entitled *Infrared and Optical Masers*, they showed the feasibility of the operation of a maser in the optical or near-infrared region, and made specific suggestions for the design of the cavity and the achievement of an inverted population.* The cavity they proposed consisted of a pair of plane reflecting surfaces placed parallel to each other, as shown in Fig. 5. The amplifying

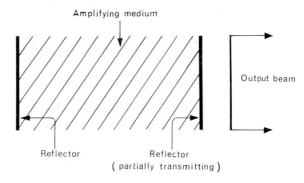

Figure 5   Basic form of the laser.

medium with an inverted population was to be placed between the reflecting surfaces. Because of the process of spontaneous emission, the amplifying medium would generate light travelling in all directions, but in the particular case of light travelling parallel to the axis of the system it would be reflected to and fro between the reflectors, and so would pass many times through the amplifying medium. Light travelling in any other direction would leave the system after a few reflections from the mirror, or perhaps without hitting them at all. Sustained oscillation could therefore be expected for light which travels to and fro perpendicularly to the mirrors.

*Editor's note: The contention that Townes and Schawlow are the inventors of the laser was challenged in the US Court of Customs and Patent Appeals during 1966. The Court decided unanimously in favour of these two scientists.

An optical cavity of this sort had long been used as a passive device (i.e. without the amplifying medium) in the Fabry-Perot interfero-meter; its use as a maser cavity in the millimetre or sub-millimetre region was suggested in 1958 by Prokhorov and by Dicke. It differs in two important respects from the conventional 'hollow box' type of resonator used in the microwave region. It has dimensions which are very large compared with the wavelength of the radiation; and it has only two reflecting ends instead of being entirely enclosed by reflect-ing walls.

The wavelength of visible light extends from about 7×10^{-5} cm to 4×10^{-5} cm (Fig. 2), so that a cavity scaled down from the usual type of microwave cavity, which is typically half a wavelength long, would have linear dimensions only of this order of magnitude. There are several objections to the use of such a cavity in the optical region; not the least significant is that it would not be possible to put into it enough amplifying medium to sustain oscillation. On the other hand, if a large cavity of this sort were used at a small wavelength it would have many resonant modes, and the amplifying medium would have to supply enough energy to sustain oscillation simultaneously in several modes.

The parallel-mirror type of resonator appears to have only one basic type of resonant mode: this is the one in which a plane wave travels to and fro in a direction parallel to the axis of the mirrors and an integral number of half-wavelengths fits into the length of the cavity. In this case it would be possible to arrange that oscillation occurred in one of these longitudinal modes only, since the medium amplifies in a narrow frequency range only. Schawlow and Townes proposed that one or both of the end mirrors could be made partially transmitting, so that a small fraction of the light wave inside the cavity could leak out.

They realized that, because the plane wave in the cavity is spatially coherent, the light coming out of the optical maser would travel in a single direction; a plane wave is equivalent to a bundle of parallel rays. The beam would spread sideways a little because of diffraction. Nevertheless, an optical maser with an aperture diameter of a centi-metre or so would have remarkable directional properties, with a typical beam spread of less than one-hundredth of a degree.

Another feature of the optical maser which Schawlow and Townes predicted is its very small spectral width. The response curve of a resonant cavity has a width which depends upon the inherent loss of the cavity (in which may be included any output taken from it). The smaller the loss, the sharper the response curve becomes (Fig. 6). When a maser is oscillating the losses are just compensated by the amplifying medium, so that the response curve becomes of vanish-ingly small width. The oscillation, apart from disturbing effects which have not so far been considered, accordingly takes place at a single frequency. The output from an optical maser would be strictly monochromatic, unlike the output of a typical discharge lamp, which consists of spontaneously emitted spectral lines, each with a spread over a frequency range of about a thousand megacycles per second. There are, however, factors which give the optical maser a finite spread of the output frequency, notably spontaneous emission from the amplifying medium.

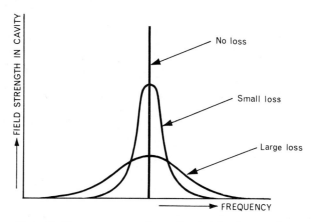

Figure 6   Response curve of a cavity, showing increased sharpness as the amount of loss is reduced.

Nevertheless, Schawlow and Townes calculated that the spread of frequencies might be as low as one-millionth of that of the spontaneous emission, or about 1 kc/s — a remarkable reduction on any previously-known light source. Such a narrow spread of frequency implies a high degree of time coherence of the output; that is, the output corresponds much more closely to a pure sine wave than does that of a conventional light source. Herein lies the importance of the optical maser to such fields as communications and long-path interferometry, discussed in later chapters.

The amplifying medium proposed by Schawlow and Townes was 'excited' potassium vapour. The upper of two levels was to be selectively excited by irradiating the vapour with light from a potassium discharge lamp. The maser transition was between this level (5P) and a lower level (3D). The 3D level has a shorter lifetime than the 5P, so that an inversion of population seemed possible. The output wavelength predicted was at 3.14 microns, in the near-infrared. A group at Columbia University under the direction of Townes started work on an optical maser of this type, but in spite of prolonged efforts the scheme was not made to work, although a somewhat similar device using caesium vapour operated at the laboratory of the Technical Research Group some time after other types of optical maser had been developed.

In the months following publication of the Schawlow and Townes paper a great deal of thought was devoted to possible schemes for making an optical maser, and a number of speculative notes were published on possible schemes, including the use of a gas discharge. The flow of these conjectural ideas became so voluminous that the editor of *Physical Review Letters* gave notice in August 1959 that future publications on masers would be restricted to those few which contained 'significant contributions to basic physics'.

A highlight of this period was the first Symposium on Quantum Electronics, held at Shawanga Lodge, High View, N.Y., in September 1959. The symposium was attended by those already established in the maser field such as Townes, Basov and Prokhorov, as well as by Schawlow and many others who were to contribute to the practical development of optical masers. Schawlow outlined the scheme he had already published, and went on to discuss solid-state optical masers using, for example, the known optical transitions in ruby near a wavelength of 7000 angstroms. He held that 'the structure of a solid-state optical maser could be especially simple. In essence, it would be just a rod with one end totally reflecting and the other end nearly so. The sides would be left clear to admit pumping radiation'.

The statement was remarkably prophetic; this is just what it turned out to be. Although most features of the optical maser were predicted before it actually operated, the possibility of a high-power output was not discussed. Schawlow mentioned the high electric field produced at a focus of a beam with a power of one milliwatt, and Gould the possibility of high-power output from a maser-type amplifier, but no-one visualized the thousands of megawatts now available from pulsed optical masers.

The ruby optical maser

Ruby consists of a crystalline aluminium oxide lattice (Al_2O_3) containing a small amount of chromium oxide (Cr_2O_3). The chromium is present in such a crystal in the form of triply-charged ions (Cr^{+++}) which are responsible for the optical effects of the otherwise colourless crystal. Fig. 7 is a simplified energy level diagram for ruby at room temperature containing 0.05 molar per cent Cr_2O_3. The optical maser transition at 6943 angstroms connects the narrow E_2 energy level with the $^4A_2$ ground state. At first sight these levels seem unsuitable for maser action, since almost all the chromium ions are normally in the ground state, and in order to achieve an inversion of population more than half of them would have to be taken out of the ground state into the E_2 state. Schawlow's proposal involved ruby

11

containing a larger proportion of chromium. In this case the energy levels are rather different from those shown, and by its use at liquid helium temperature an inversion of population seemed easier to achieve.

However, T. H. Maiman of the Hughes Aircraft Company's research laboratories at Malibu, California, showed that it was possible to achieve inversion in ruby with 0.05 per cent of chromium oxide by illuminating it with a sufficiently intense light. The chromium

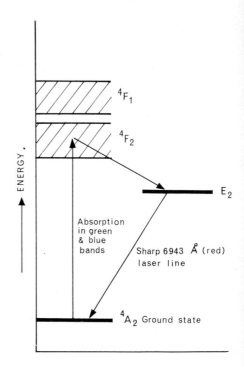

Figure 7 Simplified energy level diagram of ruby containing 0·05 molar per cent of Cr_2O_3, at room temperature.

ions absorb light in the green and blue parts of the visible spectrum (it is this absorption which gives ruby its characteristic pink or red colour) and are raised to the broad $^4F_1$ and $^4F_2$ bands; they then fall into the sharp E_2 state.

After some preliminary work on cubical samples of ruby illuminated by flashes of light, Maiman constructed the first optical maser in the form shown in Fig. 8. The ruby was in the form of a cylinder about 4 cm in length and 0.5 cm in diameter. Its ends were ground and polished plane and parallel, then partially silvered. The rod was cooled by liquid nitrogen to $-196°C$ in order to sharpen the E_2 levels and to reduce the amount of spontaneous emission to the ground state, but this was not strictly necessary, as the maser will work at room temperature. A helical flash tube provided white light in the form of a pulse which lasted about one thousandth of a second. At low light intensities the only effect was to produce a burst of spontaneous emission as the excited chromium ions fell from the E_2 state to the ground state. Above a certain critical light intensity an inversion of population was achieved and the maser oscillated, and an intense beam of red light was emitted from the ends of the rod during the flash of light from the lamp.

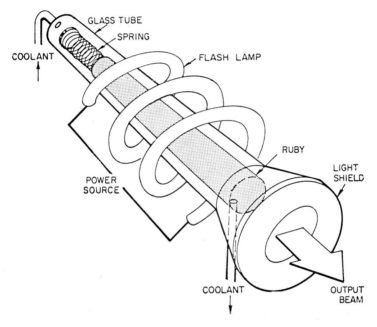

Figure 8 Form of the first ruby laser.

The beam divergence was about half a degree, and it was spatially coherent, as was demonstrated in a striking way by producing interference fringes with two slits placed in the beam; in this case the source slit used in Young's classic experiment was not needed to produce coherence. The spectral width of the radiation in the beam was one-fifth that of the spontaneously emitted red line from ruby. The power during the output pulse was nearly 10 kilowatts, so that the light flux in the beam was approaching a million times that of sunlight at the Earth's surface.

The successful operation of the first optical maser was announced by Maiman at a news conference in New York on 7th July 1960. Similar work had been in progress at the Bell Telephone Laboratories, by a team which included Schawlow, and a detailed account of the results obtained from their optical maser followed soon after. Reports of maser action in other crystals, notably those in which a host lattice is doped with a small proportion of rare-earth ions, appeared in the subsequent months. But optical masers of this type operate mainly in the near-infrared, and ruby remains the most important

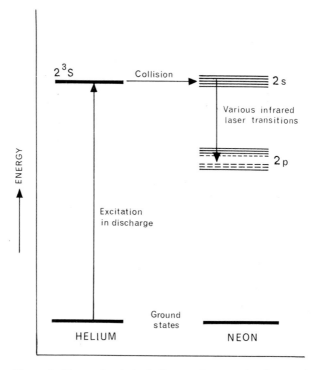

Figure 9 Energy levels in helium and neon, showing the coincidence between the metastable 2^3 s state of helium and the 2s state of neon.

material for optical masers of this high-power pulsed type. The performance of the ruby laser was subsequently considerably improved in comparison with the figures quoted above which refer only to Maiman's first model.

In 1960 the term *laser* ('light amplification by stimulated emission of radiation') was coined for the optical version of the maser; it has now almost completely superseded the term 'optical maser'. Various other terms have been suggested, such as 'iraser' for the infrared device, but none has found universal acceptance.

Gas discharge lasers

While Maiman was developing his pulsed ruby laser, work was going on at the Bell Telephone Laboratories in the field of electrical discharges. There is no doubt that much of the early thought on the possibility of the use of electrical discharges in lasers was guided by the idea that the distribution of populations of the energy levels of excited atoms in a discharge is determined by the Boltzmann relation,

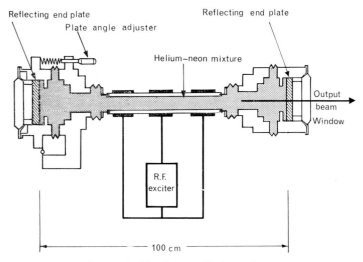

Figure 10   The first gas discharge laser.

which says that the population of an excited state of energy E is proportional to:

$$\exp - (E/KT)$$

where T in this case is the electron temperature, commonly of the order of 10,000°K in a typical discharge. Some way had to be found to disturb the conditions from this equilibrium state, in which no inversion can exist.

In the 1930s, spectroscopists had found that the distribution of populations in a discharge could be changed by mixing a second gas with the first, provided that the gases were chosen so that excitation energies were exchanged in collisions between atoms. This idea was taken up by Javan, who suggested that the population of certain energy levels in neon could be selectively increased by mixing it with helium. Helium has a metastable state 2^3S (Fig. 9) which coincides in energy almost exactly with a set of excited levels (2s) in neon. The population of the 2^3S metastable state in a helium discharge is comparatively large, and when a helium atom in this state collides with a neon atom in its ground state an exchange of energy takes place, and

15

the neon atom is left in one of the 2s states. Measurements of the lifetimes of the neon states showed that an inversion of population between the 2s and 2p states was likely, and a laser based on these principles was built (Fig. 10).

The first gas laser had plane mirrors with multi-layer dielectric coatings to give about 99 per cent reflectivity in the wavelength region where laser action was expected (about 1.15 microns). With a filling of 10 per cent neon and 90 per cent helium (atomic ratios), at a total pressure of 1 torr, the predicted oscillation was observed when the discharge was excited. In fact, oscillation occurred at five different infrared wavelengths, 1.118, 1.153, 1.160, 1.199 and 1.207 microns; the second of these was the strongest. The beam divergence was practically the theoretical diffraction-limited value of about one minute of arc, and the continuously produced power was a few milliwatts.

The spectral purity of the output of this type of laser is very high, and for brief periods the oscillation does not vary in frequency by more than 1 c/s, a remarkable performance in view of the fact that the oscillation frequency is close to 3×10^{14} c/s. The oscillation frequency is, however, largely controlled by the optical distance between the mirrors, so that vibrations, fluctuations of the discharge intensity, and the effects of temperature on the mirror supports contribute to vary the frequency of the output.

The helium-neon gas discharge laser, announced by Javan, Bennett and Herriott in February 1961, marked the beginning of rapid developments in this field. Laser action was discovered in the helium-neon system at 6328 angstroms, a visible red wavelength, and further in the infrared at 3.39 microns. It was found that laser action also occurred in discharges in pure gases, showing a condition in these far removed from the expected Boltzmann equilibrium. The discovery of new laser systems was made considerably easier by the use of concave reflectors at the ends of the cavity, and the form of the resonant modes of various types of cavity has been worked out by Fox, Li Boyd, Gordon and others. The tolerance in the alignment of concave mirror cavities is far less critical than for those which use plane reflectors, and the diffraction loss is smaller, so that a lower gain system can be used. Pulsed gas discharge systems have been found to give laser action during or after the excitation pulse, at wavelengths which cannot be produced under steady conditions.

A very large number of wavelengths are now available from continuous or pulsed gas discharge lasers; the range extends from a few tenths of a millimetre through the far-infrared and the visible into the near-ultraviolet. Laser action has been achieved in a variety of ways and in a variety of materials, including semiconductors; details of these developments are given in subsequent chapters.

The basic principle on which both the maser and the laser rely was known some thirty-five years before the first maser was operated. At that time techniques did not exist for exploiting the principle, neither was sufficient known about energy levels. As technology advanced and data became available, the way was opened for constructive thinking about stimulated emission devices. It might be claimed that the laser is such a simple device it could have been invented long ago; but this is a case where a touch of brilliance was needed to realize what, with hindsight, seems so obvious.

2

THE NATURE OF LASER LIGHT[7]

C. C. EAGLESFIELD

Standard Telecommunication Laboratories, Harlow

Apart from its great intensity, the light emitted by a laser is remarkable for being 'coherent'. In other words, it is composed of regular and continuous waves, like those emitted at much lower frequencies by radio transmitters, and in this respect it is quite different from the incoherent light emitted by any other source of light — whether stars, candles or electric lamps. What, then, are the differences between coherent light and incoherent light on the one hand, and between coherent light and coherent radiation at lower frequencies, on the other?

Ordinary incoherent light is a kind of 'noise' — energy in a chaotic form. Indeed, from white light engineers have borrowed the term 'white noise', to mean noise spread over a wide range of frequencies. In communications engineering one is usually interested in a moderate band of frequencies, often in a narrow band. That is, one is interested in the output of a narrow-band filter which stops most of the white noise and allows only noise near a chosen frequency to pass through.

Fig. 11(a) shows schematically narrow-band noise consisting of a wave of roughly a constant frequency, but of a fluctuating amplitude. The curve below it, Fig. 11(b), shows the probability of occurrence of a given amplitude: it will be seen that amplitude variations of two or three to one are common.

The oscillator of an ordinary radio transmitter produces, by contrast, a wave of roughly constant frequency and roughly constant amplitude. These conditions are achieved, in effect, by passing noise through both a frequency filter and an amplitude filter. Fig. 12 indicates the arrangement of an oscillator. Noise is amplified and passed through a filter and a 'limiter', and there is a feedback link to the input. Of course, the three operations of amplifying, filtering and limiting may be merged in practice, and generally it is a saturation of the amplifier that performs the limiting.

Thus, mere frequency filtering is not sufficient to change noise to a coherent wave: it still remains noise. The output of an oscillator,

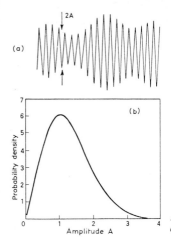

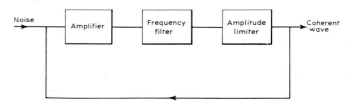

Figure 11 The waveform (*a*) and amplitude distribution (*b*) of narrow band noise.

however, is something that is generally recognized as approximately coherent. In practice, we shall never get a wave of a single frequency and a constant amplitude, but we may approach nearer and nearer to that ideal.

Now while the random amplitude of ordinary thermal light puts a very severe limitation on its use for, say, communication, it is nevertheless true, of course, that it is possible to get interference effects — that is, the addition or subtraction of two waves — with thermal light. It is this point, perhaps, which leads to some confusion between people brought up on radio and microwaves and those with a background in optics.

The reason why interference can arise with thermal light is as follows: As is indicated in Fig. 11(a), the amplitude changes smoothly, and so does the frequency. For a short time the wave can be regarded as coherent, and the length of this 'coherence time' is approximately equal to the reciprocal bandwidth of the filter. For interference to occur the light must be 'collimated' — that is, put in a parallel beam. In practice this is done by passing the light through a pair of apertures. The shorter the coherence time, the greater is the required

Figure 12 Schematic arrangement of an oscillator.

19

collimation; in other words, the apertures must be smaller or placed farther apart.

Meaning of coherency

Now let use see how coherent light fits into the general picture of coherent sources. Fig. 13 shows the growth of the art of generating coherent wave-forms over the last 130 years. Each point on the chart represents a significant upward jump in frequency associated with

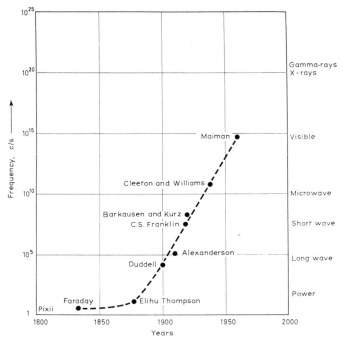

Figure 13 The development in the art of generating coherent wave-forms.

the name of a man or men; some of the names may not be very familiar and, as only coherent sources are shown on this chart, certain better known names are absent. For instance, Hertz, the discoverer of radio waves, is not there; his experiments were made with spark sources, which are incoherent.

Faraday started the whole thing with his d.c. (zero frequency) generator. Next we have Pixii who, in the following year, made the first a.c. generator — although he did not want a.c. and quickly invented the commutator to convert it to d.c. The frequency was presumably a few cycles per second.

It was then many years before any higher frequency was made, and for the next point I pick Elihu Thompson, a pioneer of power generation, whose generators worked at 16 c/s. The date was 1878.

A very significant date is 1900, when Duddell invented the arc transmitter for radio. The arc saturated at a certain amplitude and consequently imposed amplitude limitation. The resulting waveform was coherent, and it was possible to modulate the transmitters with speech and even music. Duddell's arc worked at 10 kc/s; but arc transmitters were later developed by Poulsen to 100 kc/s. However, for that frequency I choose to put Alexanderson, with his remarkable electro-mechanical alternator; he reached 100 kc/s by 1909.

By 1906 the thermionic valve had been invented by Lee de Forest; it gradually replaced the arc transmitter. For my next point I pick C. S. Franklin, who was experimenting with propagation using early valve generators and reached 30 Mc/s in 1919. Franklin was working as Marconi's assistant, and it is interesting that he gets a place on the chart and not Marconi, whose more personal early work was done with spark transmitters.

A rather important advance was made in 1920, with the Barkhausen and Kurz positive-grid triode valve, which broke into the region of frequencies where the finite velocity of the electrons has to be taken into account. They reached 300 Mc/s.

Then, by 1936, Cleeton and Williams reached 47 gigacycles (47×10^9 c/s: 6.4 mm wavelength) with low-power magnetrons. Finally in 1960 we have Maiman with visible radiation at 500 teracycles (5×10^{14} c/s). Coherent light is merely the highest frequency in the spectrum that has so far been generated coherently; if the curve of Fig. 13 is extrapolated we may expect progress into the ultraviolet and X-ray regions.

Properties of light

At this stage it is convenient to recall some of the properties of ordinary light. The first thing is that the wavelength is extremely small in comparison with radio, which means that devices such as lenses and reflectors of convenient size have a very great diameter when measured in wavelengths; consequently very narrow beams of light can be made. An extreme case is the 200-inch reflector on Mount Palomar with its diameter of 10 million wavelengths. To give a beam of the same narrowness, a microwave reflector for 1 cm waves would need to be sixty-five miles in diameter.

Another consequence of the very small wavelength is the very small spot to which the light can be focused, of the order of a few wavelengths in diameter. To get such a small spot with a conventional light source, such as a hot filament, the source itself must be very small or else its various parts will not act together. This is simply an example of the collimation that is necessary with thermal light, to which I have already referred; it puts a limit to the concentration of power per unit area in the spot, which can only be increased by raising the temperature of the source — and here, too, there are practical limits.

With a source of coherent light — a laser, that is — the various parts can be phased in much the same way as the elements of a radio aerial are phased, and it is possible to combine a large source with a minute spot. A very high concentration of power is perfectly feasible, and this accounts for the popular view of lasers as devices for burning small holes, particularly in razor blades! But more useful applications are being found, such as the spot-welding of very small parts and the machining of difficult materials or of very intricate patterns (see Chapter 7).

When one has coherent light, one becomes more directly conscious of its high frequency; this is shown vividly with the doppler effect, whereby relative movements of a source and a detector result in changes in frequency. A relative movement of one mile per hour give a doppler frequency shift of nearly a megacycle; this may be of great value for measuring velocities, but it may be inconvenient in, for instance, a communications system where source and receiver are moving rapidly at varying speeds.

The very high frequency is obviously attractive for communications since such enormous bandwidths are available for carrying information of many kinds. In principle we can put the whole previously available frequency spectrum, up to microwaves, on to a single optical carrier, and even that would occupy only a small part of the optical band; and we can have as many optical beams as we like.

Techniques of high frequencies

Big changes of frequency, however, require big changes in technique. Consider first the methods of generation: at power frequencies, rotating machines are universally used. For long radio waves, although machines were once used, the normal methods use valve generators of such simple types that one need not consider electron transit times. For short waves, one is approaching the region where special valves such as magnetrons are necessary. At microwaves, the electronic methods are supplemented by molecular methods — by masers, that is. And in the visible region, molecular and atomic devices — lasers — come into their own.

This change of technique is also shown in the way in which operations, familiar at lower frequencies, are carried out at light frequencies. Light can be detected by photo-electric devices such as photocathodes, which are virtually quantum counters; these are not available at lower frequencies. Moreover, these photoelectric devices can be used for frequency changing: microwave 'beats' between two optical signals have been demonstrated, and also the sum frequency, in the form of a third visible frequency. Transparent materials which exhibit a change of refractive index under the influence of an electric field are commonly used for modulators. A consequence of the concentration possible with coherent light is that harmonics of substantial intensity can be produced using such transparent materials, and also in reflections from suitable surfaces.

Turning now to a property of light that is not so favourable, perhaps the biggest snag confronting anyone who wishes to use lasers for communications is noise. Typical noise at power frequencies is that caused by switching; at long wavelengths it is typically atmospheric; and at short wavelengths the reception of radiation is much troubled by sunspots. By the time we reach microwaves the most important noise is thermal in origin, and at optical frequencies it is 'quantum noise' — the effect of the arrival, at the receiver, of individual photons of light.

Now, quantum noise power is proportional to frequency, so it might be supposed that for all applications a high frequency is undesirable. If we consider, however, a point-to-point communications system in which the size of the aerials remains the same and the frequency is varied, we find that the received signal power goes up as the square of the frequency. Thus while quantum noise is a snag, it has not removed the advantage of going to a higher frequency, but merely reduced it. This effect is even more pronounced with radar, where the power received from the target is proportional to the fourth power of the frequency.

Granular effect

A quite different effect, one that is very characteristic of laser light — though not, as we shall see, peculiar to it — is the 'granular effect'. It shows up when almost any object is viewed by the light of a continuous visible gas laser[3-7]. Apparently it was quite unexpected by the inventors of the gas laser and took them by surprise. Different observers saw the effect differently, some seeing it as dark spots on a light background and some as bright spots on a dark background.

The explanation of the granular effect seems to be as shown in Fig. 14. Light falling normally in a very smooth surface is reflected, if at all, only in one direction, with very little scattering. If the observer is looking from one side, as in Fig. 14(a), the surface appears uniformly dark.

The situation is very different when the surface is rough. Fig. 14(b) shows a rough surface, illuminated by a coherent plane wave. Now, each element of the surface will scatter the light in a rather complicated way which depends on the detail of its roughness, and,

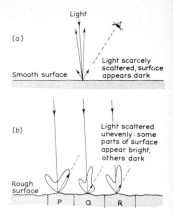

Figure 14 Light is scarcely scattered by a smooth surface (*a*) but each element of rough surface (*b*) scatters differently.

generally speaking, each part of the surface is different. According to how strong the scattering is in the direction of view, the element may appear bright or dark. Thus, in this case, P is bright, Q is rather dim and R is dark — hence the granular appearance.

The size of the granulations depends on the size of the elements that the eye (or the camera lens) can resolve; successive photographs of the same surface illuminated by laser light, taken with decreasing camera aperture, and hence diminishing resolution, show bigger and bigger granulations.

Let us now consider a little more carefully by eye. In Fig. 14 the direction of view is shown as being the same for each element. In fact it is not the same, as can be seen in Fig. 15. The elements of the surface PQR become pqr on the retina, with a slightly different angle of view for each. However, whether the element is bright or dark still depends on how the angle of view tallies with the polar diagram. The surface still appears granulated.

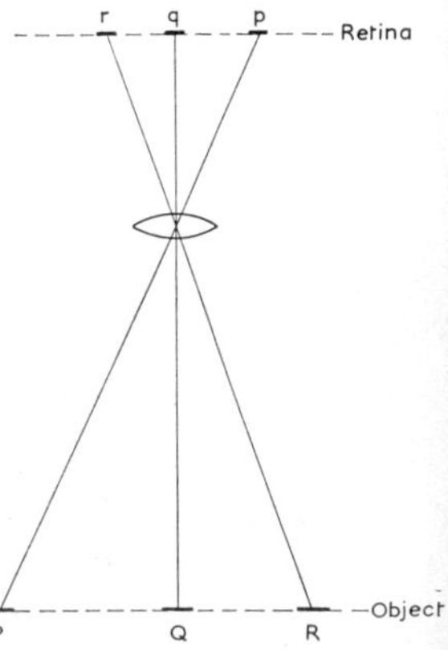

Figure 15 Spots on the retina arise from elements of the surface. The elements are small if the eye is focused on the surface (see also Figure 16).

24

When the eye is not focused on the surface, Fig. 16, the light reaching p can start from anywhere in the area P, but of course the light from each element of P has to be going in the right direction. Clearly the areas P, Q, etc, overlap, but I have not shown this in the diagram, to avoid confusion.

There is rather a strange visual effect associated with defocusing. If one moves one's head slowly a small distance, the granulations appear to move across the object. It results from parallax between the object plane and the focus plane. The movement can be in either direction, depending on whether the eye is focused above or below the object. It is not very easy to focus one's eyes on the surface because one's eye tends to 'chase' the spots, so that this relative movement is rather commonly seen.

I have described all these visual effects as though they were novel

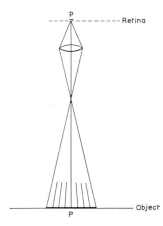

Figure 16   Individual elements are much enlarged when the focus is shifted (see also Figure 15).

and only recently found with laser light. In fact, it seems they were observed many years ago.

I explained earlier that interference effects are found with ordinary light as long as it is well collimated. The degree of collimation necessary is greater for wideband sources, but I am told that granulation can be observed even with sunlight. It seems to be necessary that the polar diagrams of the surface elements, indicated in Fig. 14(b), should be the same for all wavelengths in the source; this may not be so for all surfaces, however, and it seems possible that not all surfaces appear granulated in collimated sunlight.

The very narrow bandwidth and, of course, its intensity make laser light ideal for observing granulations, and the reader with access to a visible gas laser will find it fascinating to look at, particularly with an eyeglass or a low-power microscope. A particularly interesting effect should be obtained with several lasers of different colours. If their beams are inclined to each other, the bright spots of each colour would tend to come at different places and one should see a rather rich granulation of the different colours.

Holography

However, the granular appearance, when viewed in laser light, of ordinary matt surfaces, although startling, would not add to one's understanding of a scene illuminated in this way; in fact, the reverse is obviously the case. I shall now introduce another very interesting effect, where a surface which in ordinary light would appear to have merely a fine grain-like structure, can have concealed in it, as it were in code, a view which appears as an intelligible picture when laser light is directed upon it.

The way in which this can be devised depends originally on the method of 'microscopy by reconstructed wavefronts' of Gabor,[8] a paper written at a time when the nearest to a coherent light source was the mercury lamp. It has been developed and refined since by later workers, particularly by Leith and Upatnieks,[9] who had the advantage of being able to work with laser light in their later work. Professor Gabor discusses the new science of holography in greater detail in Chapter 5.

The principle of the process is shown in Fig. 17, in several stages of refinement. It consists essentially in forming a diffraction pattern, or 'hologram' as Gabor called it, of the original. Ideally, the hologram contains all the information from which the original can be reconstructed.

In Fig. 17(a) the hologram of a photographic transparency is made by sending a beam of coherent light through it on to a photographic film placed far enough away that there is substantial diffraction. For instance, the transparency might be 1 cm across and the film 1 metre away from it. The reconstruction is done by sending the same beam of light through the hologram, and a real image of it is formed, for instance, on another photographic film. The image is, ideally, a reproduction of the transparency but in practice the quality, by this simple method, is not very good, the reason being that the hologram records the amplitude of the light falling on the film at any one spot, but does not record its phase. A record of the phase is necessary for a good reconstruction.

Gabor pointed out that if the transparency is such that it permits a substantial amount of the original beam of light to pass through it unchanged, so that the diffraction pattern of the transparency is added vectorially to a uniform coherent background, then in fact a record of the phase is built into the hologram, and the reconstruction is quite good.

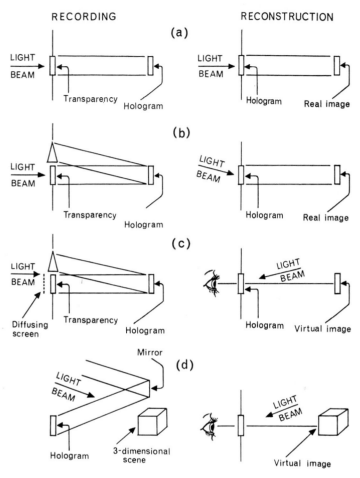

Figure 17 Principles of holography, in several stages of refinement

However, a more potent way of providing the coherent background is shown in Fig. 17(b), where a double beam is used, the second beam being derived by bending round part of the original beam. This is virtually only feasible with laser light. Now the two beams interfere to form a grating on the hologram, which in the reconstruction process bends the beam of light as shown in Fig. 17(b). However, instead of being quite a uniform grating, the intensity and spacing of the lines of the grating vary, owing to the transparency, and again a real image is formed, displaced off the direction of the beam, as shown. The quality of the image is greatly improved by this expedient.

A further development is shown in Fig. 17(c), where a diffusing screen is put in front of the transparency. This has a number of important effects. First it ensures that the coherent background is supplied entirely by the second deflected beam, and also it magnifies the diffraction of the transparency. The hologram acquires a quite different appearance; in methods Fig. 17(a) and 17(b) the coarse structure of the transparency tends to persist in the hologram, but in Fig. 17(c) the pattern on the hologram is completely homogeneous and always has the same appearance whatever the subject matter on the transparency. This appearance has a fine grain-like structure.

This is the appearance in ordinary ligh' however. When, in the reconstruction process, the coherent light beam is sent through the hologram, a virtual image can be seen by eye, reconstructing the original transparency. As Leith and Upatnieks remark, if one looks directly by eye at a transparency illuminated by a point source of light, only the very small part of it is seen which is directly in line with the point of light, but if one puts a diffuser behind the transparency, the whole of it becomes visible. Here it is as though the diffusing screen had been transformed across with the transparency and the hologram were illuminated by diffused light.

Three-dimensional holograms

A still further development is to record the diffused reflected light from a three-dimensional scene on to the hologram. The second beam is now more conveniently deflected by a mirror, as shown in Fig. 17(d). Again the hologram may be viewed directly by eye, and it has the property of appearing three-dimensional as in stereo photography, although in this case there is only the one hologram rather than the usual pair of stereo photographs. Moreover, if the observer moves his head, he sees a change in perspective and a parallax between near and far objects matching that which would occur in viewing the original scene. One can actually look round an obstructing object to see what lies behind.

For illuminating a scene in depth, the laser must be very coherent and it is desirable that it should be single-mode; also, if there is any chance of movement in the scene, the laser should be pulsed with a very short pulse.

It will be realized that the colour of the reconstruction is that of the light beam used. The hologram itself is black-and-white. Hence if the original transparency were black and white, it would be reconstructed not in black-and-white but in black and red, or whatever colour the laser gives. Similarly, the three-dimensional scene is reconstructed, as originally illuminated, in red. Leith and Upatnieks suggest that it may be possible to make reconstructions in full colour by illuminating the scene by each of the three primary colours and viewing the hologram in beams of the same colours. In this way a three-dimensional scene

28

could be recorded on a black-and-white hologram and viewed as a three-dimensional image in full colour.

Summarizing the contents of this chapter, it can be said that laser light is simply an extremely high radio frequency. Yet the size of the jump from the previously available microwaves is so great that many new effects come into play. The manipulations customary at microwaves take on a new look when performed at such high frequencies and short wavelengths.

In another sense, laser light is only a very monochromatic visible radiation. Here again, the jump from the previously available monochromatic sources is so great that rather startling visual effects appear. Since vision is such an important part of our lives, the visual effects are perhaps the more impressive.

3

SOLID-STATE AND GAS LASERS

Dr D. W. GOODWIN

Royal Radar Establishment, Malvern

The feasibility of laser action, as we learned in Chapter 1, was demonstrated in the first instance by Dr T. H. Maiman in 1960,[11] who succeeded in producing pulsed oscillations when exciting a dilute ruby crystal with a xenon photographic flash tube. Shortly afterwards Javan and his colleagues demonstrated continuous laser action in a tube containing a mixture of helium and neon gases.[12] Since then laser emission has been observed in many solids 'doped' with various impurities, and the laser emission lines found in gases are now too numerous to catalogue.

It is fair to assert that the progress in development of these two types of laser has been extensive, yet in many respects they are complementary. Although powers of tens of watts have been achieved using neodymium-doped yttrium aluminium garnet (YAG) at 1.065 microns and in gaseous carbon dioxide (10.6 microns), the gas laser gives a more coherent output than its solid-state counterpart, and is much easier to operate continuously. On the other hand, because of the long fluorescent lifetimes common in a solid-state laser, much higher pulsed output powers and energies are available. Powers in excess of 1 gigawatt (1000 megawatts) have been produced in a pulse extending for 30 nanoseconds.

It is my purpose in this chapter to compare and contrast in detail both the mode of operation and the properties of solid-state and gaseous lasers, and to select for particular reference those which, so far, have shown the more promising characteristics for general use.

Solid-state lasers

The energy states in which a free ion can exist consist of groups of sharp levels which are split by spins and orbital angular moments of the electrons associated with the particular ion. In general, inter-actions between levels are small and, typically, linewidths of emission are broadened by the doppler effect to the order of 0.3 cm^{-1} (~ 800

Mc/s) in width;* whilst fluorescent decay times are less than one microsecond.

The effect of putting a free ion into a solid is to modify the energy level structure and so affect both the fluorescent linewidth and the lifetime. The magnitude of the effect depends upon the particular ion which is incorporated within the solid matrix. In the case of a 'transition' ion such as trivalent chromium, where no shielding of the 3d shell exists, the energy levels are modified considerably by the internal electric field of the lattice. In general, for the transition ions the displacement due to the crystal field is of the order of 1000 cm^{-1}, whilst that due to spin orbit interaction is only about 100 cm^{-1}.

Electronic transitions in the rare earth ions, however, occur in the shielded 5f shell. In this case displacements due to crystal fields are of the order of 100 cm^{-1}, whilst those due to spin orbit interactions are considerably greater — up to 2000 cm^{-1}.

Because of these various interactions, the transition probabilities between various levels are modified considerably and many *metastable* levels are found to exist, for which the transition probability is reduced considerably. Lifetimes up to 80 milliseconds are not uncommon. The fluorescent linewidth is governed by interactions between the ion and the thermal vibrations of the lattice. Usually linewidths decrease rapidly with decreasing temperature until a linewidth that is independent of temperature is reached. We shall now consider laser action in a three-level system, using ruby as a typical example.

The ruby laser

Ruby consists of chromium trioxide dissolved in aluminium oxide. Chromium ions are contained within the lattice substitutionally for the aluminium site to the extent of 0.05 atomic per cent. The chromium ion is triply charged and has an energy level diagram as shown in Fig. 7. The intense absorption bands exist in the green and blue (due to which ruby is red in colour). A simple arrangement for exciting a ruby is shown in Fig. 18, where a rod typically 2 inches long and $\frac{1}{4}$ inch in diameter, having highly polished ends flat to an accuracy of 500 angstroms, and with ends parallel to 2 seconds, is held between two xenon flash tubes by a reflecting aluminium foil wrapping. The ends of the rod have highly reflecting coatings.

During the light flash, which should be of shorter duration than the fluorescent lifetime (2 milliseconds), ions are excited into the 'pump' bands, from where they lose energy to the lattice and are transferred to the 2E metastable levels. Ions can then decay to the 2A ground state by fluorescence.

In order to achieve laser action it is necessary that the lasing media has a negative absorption coefficient; that is, that it becomes an

* One micron is 10^{-6} metres and equal to $10,000 \text{ cm}^{-1}$.

amplifier. This condition can be achieved only by transferring more than half the total number of ions within the rod into the metastable level. Under these conditions stimulated emission is possible.

Because of the large number of ions needed in the metastable state ($> 5 \times 10^{-18}$), the threshold for laser action is very large, of the order of 50 to 100 joules in an efficient resonator. Nevertheless, by careful choice of resonator, and by efficient pumping and coating, continuous laser action has been reported with threshold powers of less than a kilowatt.

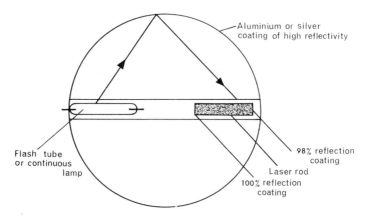

Figure 18 Simple ellipsoidal 'pumping' arrangement for a ruby laser.

Provided the absorption coefficient in the pump band is less than the reciprocal of the radius of the rod, which is to say that the rod is optically thin, then the amount of pump light absorbed will be proportional to the chromium concentration in the ruby. We have also seen that the threshold absorbed energy will be proportional to the concentration, and so to a first order approximation in ruby the threshold energy, as measured by the energy dissipated in the flash tube, will be independent of concentration. Because of the very high gain in ruby due to its having to transfer a large number of ions into the metastable state, the threshold will also be independent of losses within the crystal. However, the amount of energy emitted will depend on the ratio of the loss of the actual resonator in which the active rod is situated to the total loss of the system. For a particular input energy, the highest output efficiency is achieved with the lowest threshold, highest possible concentration and lowest internal loss.

The main disadvantage of a three-level laser system is its high pulsed light threshold energy. For many applications a continuous source is required. The threshold power needed for continuous laser action is equal to the threshold energy under pulsed conditions divided by the fluorescent lifetime — and for ruby this can be prohibitively high. However, by improvements in crystal quality, and by the use of sophisticated cavities of ellipsoidal form, continuous action has been achieved in ruby with a threshold of 830 kilowatts at room temperature.

The four-level laser

The number of ions needed to be in the metastable level in order to produce population inversion can be reduced by the use of a terminal level which, unlike the ground state, is relatively unpopulated. The terminal level needs to be at least 1000 cm^{-1} above the ground state in order to achieve a low threshold energy at or around room temperature. The number of ions in the terminal level is governed by Boltzmann's law, which states that under conditions of thermal equilibrium the ratio of ions in the terminal to ground state is equal to

$$\exp - (E/KT)$$

where E is the energy separation, K is Boltzmann's constant and T is the absolute temperature (see also page 15). Trivalent neodymium, one of the most widely used rare earth ions, has a separation between terminal and ground state of 2000 cm^{-1}. Hence the number of ions in the terminal state is a thousandth of those in the ground state. Under these conditions the laser threshold energy becomes critically dependent upon the losses within the system, and in order to take full advantage of the likely reduction in threshold the total optical loss must be reduced to a minimum.

The losses which are likely to occur within a solid-state laser are due to a variety of causes. It is inevitable that some loss will occur because there has to be some transmission from the laser rod out of one end. Both the threshold energy and output depend on the total loss and there is little point in reducing the reflector loss to below 10 per cent of the internal loss within the laser rod.

The majority of host lattices are high-melting-point materials, usually difficult to obtain in the pure state. For instance, most alkaline earth fluorides contain large quantities of oxides and other halogens, whilst the rare earth fluorides contain differing amounts of oxyfluorides. Such impurities are usually precipitated during the growth process. Being precipitates about 1 micron in diameter, and having a refractive index differing from that of the host lattice, these impurities are effective scattering centres for the stimulated emission, and so constitute a significant loss term. By measuring the single pass loss as a function of wavelength the density and refractive index of the scatterers can be deduced.

Many host lattices are anisotropic in refractive index. Large changes in refractive index can occur due to the non-uniform distribution of the dopant and, where needed, its compensating impurity.

Such changes in refractive index can disperse the stimulated light beam, and lead to losses in excess of 5 per cent per centimetre in such materials as calcium tungstate and other anisotropic lattices.

Because of its geometry, the injected light is focused in such a way as to be concentrated at the centre of a rod. Provided there is little scatter or anisotropy, the centre of a rod will exhibit laser action first. Because of its small section, the diffraction loss will be particularly high in the portion of rod that lases first, causing an artificially increased threshold, and resulting in a small slope efficiency of output energy.

The neodymium laser

The trivalent neodymium ion has now been incorporated into a great many lattices, both substitutionally and by compensating techniques. Typical examples of substitutional lattices are yttrium aluminium

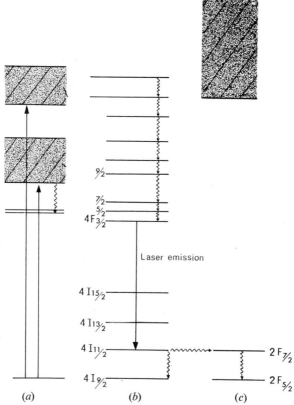

Figure 19 Energy level diagrams for (*a*) trivalent chromium (*b*) trivalent neodymium, (*c*) trivalent cerium ion; indicating resonant transfer into the neodymium ion.

garnet ($Y_3Al_5O_{12}$) and lanthanum fluoride (LaF_3); and of compensated lattices, calcium fluoride (CaF_2, with O^{2+} and F^- compensation) and calcium tungstate ($CaWO_4$, with sodium compensation).

The energy level diagram for the trivalent neodymium ion is shown in Fig. 19. These levels are all associated with the inner 4f shell, which is screened from external fields by the 5d and 6s outer shells. As a result of this screen the lower levels are very narrow and both absorption and fluorescent emission lines are narrow. However, some upper levels are broadened by interaction with the 5d configuration, which is at a frequency around 30,000 cm^{-1}. The amount of mixing depends on the particular type of lattice. For instance, the pump bands for laser action around 15,000 cm^{-1} are much more intense in calcium tungstate than in YAG. In fact the more effective pumping bands for YAG are the $^4F_{5/2}$ and $^4F_{7/2}$ levels.

Owing to the crystal field, the $^4F_{3/2}$ level is split into a doublet, the magnitude of the splitting depending upon the crystal field. Fluorescence occurs from this level down to the four multiplets of the ground state. However, the transition probabilities are such that the fluorescence to the $^4I_{11/2}$ is nearly an order of magnitude stronger than to other members of the multiplet. The $^4I_{11/2}$ level is roughly 2000 cm^{-1} above the ground state and at room temperature is virtually depopulated. Transitions to the ground state appear to be by a fast non-radiative process.

The threshold for pulsed and, where applicable, continuous laser action for the trivalent neodymium ion in a variety of host lattices is given in Table 1. The actual threshold values depend upon a variety of causes, such as strength of pump band, fluorescent linewidth and the relative optical quality of the lattice. We will deal with these various quantities in turn.

Table 1. Pulsed and continuous-wave threshold for the trivalent neodymium in various host lattices

Host lattice	Temp. °K	Frequency (cm^{-1})	Pulsed threshold (joules)	Continuous threshold (watts)
$CaWO_4$[3]	290	9380	0.5	430
CaF_2	290	9432	15	
$Ca(NbO_3)_2$[5]	77	9432	2	
YAG_4	290	9420	≈0.2	90
$YGaG_4$	290	9420	250	
$YGaG_4$	290	9420	350	
Y_2O_3[6]	290	9300	250	
Y_2O_3[6]	290	9260	350	
Gd_2O_3[7]	290	9260	9	
CeF_3	290	9370	3	

As yet, our understanding of the oscillator strengths of the pump bands is inadequate, and it is not yet possible to predict in which lattice the oscillator strength is large. Observation shows that the strongest visible pump bands appear in the tungstates and molybdates.

Large variations in fluorescent linewidth occur as a function of the lattice. It was thought initially that as the Debye temperature of a lattice decreased, so the lattice vibrational energy would decrease, and so the linewidth would decrease. In fact, just the opposite appears to be true. The nature of the phonon interaction has not yet been discovered, but it is believed to be due to vibrational interactions between the two split $^4F_{3/2}$ levels. It is apparent that, as the separation between these levels is increased by the internal crystalline field, so the linewidth is decreased to a minimum of 5.3 cm^{-1} at room temperature in YAG.

Further reductions in linewidth for the $^4F_{3/2} \rightarrow {}^4I_{11/2}$ transition in neodymium, it is thought, will be achieved in complex lattices with higher internal crystalline fields than in YAG, but whether this can be achieved without decreasing the fluorescent lifetime or decreasing the optical quality of the lattice remains to be seen.

The optical quality of the lattice in which the neodymium ion is incorporated is of considerable importance for, in a four-level system such as exists in trivalent neodymium, the threshold energy is that energy needed to overcome the losses within the system. As we are looking for a lattice in which the ion is situated in a site of low symmetry, there is a high probability of the lattice being anisotropic — as is the case with calcium tungstate and calcium molybdate. For these materials, the major loss mechanism is optical divergence within the laser rod, sometimes by as much as 8 minutes of arc,[13] leading to a loss of stimulating radiation and an increase in threshold.

In YAG, however, which has a pseudo-cubic structure, the trivalent neodymium ion is situated in a low symmetry site, and rods of good optical quality can be obtained. In such rods, scatter of radiation becomes important, and in order to obtain the lowest possible thresholds and the highest possible efficiencies, scatter losses need to be below 0.3 per cent per centimetre of laser rod. If we assume that the particle sizes are roughly the same as the wavelength of the emitted radiation, then the number of scattering centres needs to be below 100,000 per cubic centimetre. As the centres are likely to be due to impurity precipitates or solute trails, the highest possible chemical purity of starting material is called for — and the highest skills in crystal growth.

In order to exploit a laser fully, both as a powerful continuous source and as a generator of high-powered pulses, it is necessary to achieve high population inversion ratios momentarily. Because of the relatively weak pump bands, it appears possible to pump no more than a small percentage of the ground state ions into the metastable state, even using the most powerful sources obtainable. Some improvement can be obtained using *resonant transfer*.

Resonant transfer

The spectral emission of both flash tubes and continuously emitting lamps extends over a wide range of the visible spectrum, and only a small fraction of their light is usefully absorbed by ions having predominantly 4f transitions. But it is possible for an ion having intense visible absorption bands — such as a transition ion (3d) or a divalent rare earth (5d, 6s), or an actinide (6d, 5f) — to be incorporated into a lattice and to transfer its energy directly to a trivalent rare earth; typical examples include trivalent chromium to trivalent neodymium in YAG, or trivalent erbium to either trivalent holmium or trivalent thulium in erbium-doped YAG. There are in fact many known examples of resonant transfer in glasses, but few are of practical use in laser systems at the present time.

As shown in Fig. 19, trivalent chromium has two very intense absorption bands in the green and blue regions of the spectrum. Ions are easily pumped into these levels and are either transferred directly to the neodymium ion or reach it via a metastable level, a process which seems the more likely. That the trivalent chromium ions are useful for resonant transfer is seen from their own ability as a laser ion. For instance, as it is a three-level system at least 50 per cent of the ground state ions have to reach the metastable level in order to achieve population inversion. Secondly, in order to achieve resonant transfer the activator must hold energy in the metastable state for a time longer than the transfer time, which appears to be of the order of 100 microseconds. Trivalent chromium has a lifetime of the order of a few milliseconds, and so fulfills this requirement as well.

The chromium ion can enter the YAG lattice substitutionally for the aluminium ion. Provided the relatively low concentrations of neodymium and chromium needed can be made to occupy adjacent sites in the unit cell, resonable reductions in continuous threshold powers should be achieved. Thresholds have been reduced by a factor of two using trivalent chromium as the coactivator in YAG.[14]

There is obviously a much greater opportunity of achieving resonant transfer if the coactivating ion is already present in the unit cell, and its concentration maintains a reasonably long fluorescent lifetime and has a resonable absorption coefficient in the visible (that is, approximately the inverse of the rod diameter). Such is the case with a mixture of YAG and ErAG. Both trivalent holmium and trivalent thulium have been incorporated into this lattice. As these ions become four-level systems at 77°K, they achieve low thresholds only at this temperature. Threshold powers as low as 57 watts have been recorded.

Another lattice in which the coactivating ion exists in the unit cell is cerium fluoride. Resonant transfer takes place from the ultraviolet and near-visible regions via the trivalent cerium into the trivalent neodymium. The cerium ion has a $^2F_{7/2}$ level which is coincidental in energy with the terminal state of the neodymium ion and leads to some fluorescent line broadening of the $^4F_{2/3} \rightarrow ^4I_{11/2}$ transition in the neodymium ion.

The transfer of energy from the pump band to metastable level of the coactivator occurs by *multiphonon emission*; energy which is absorbed directly by the lattice. There is obviously little advantage in using a coactivator which absorbs at a frequency much greater than the metastable level of the lasing ion otherwise excessive lattice heating will occur.

The divalent rare earths

We have discussed at length the lasing properties of the trivalent rare earth ions, and in particular neodymium, because of its importance as a continuous-wave material that lases at room temperature. Certain divalent rare earth ions, however, have interesting properties, although so far no suitable lattice has been found for their exploitation at room temperature.

Three ions have been usefully employed so far — samarium, thulium and dysprosium. Their energy level schemes bear some resemblance to their trivalent equivalent with which they are iso-electronic, and they have all been successfully incorporated in the divalent calcium site in calcium fluoride. Normally the rare earth exists in a trivalent state, with interstitial fluorine compensation; but, either by j-irradiation or more permanently using high-temperature electrolysis the interstitial fluorine compensator can be removed from the lattice, leaving the rare earth ion in the divalent state.

Because the charge on the ion has been decreased, the broad 5d and 6s levels drop from around 30,000 to 10,000 cm^{-1}, and so constitute a useful pump band for levels with infrared transitions. At low temperatures, when phonon interactions are reduced, the fluorescent lines are very narrow indeed — less than the separation of the cavity modes ($\sim$0.02 cm^{-1}). As narrow fluorescent lines can be effectively broadened by an inhomogeneous magnetic field the threshold power can be varied, and by this means giant pulses can be generated from a continuously pumped laser.

A list of the properties of divalent rare earth ion lasers is given in Table 2. Because of the close proximity of the broad pump band some absorption occurs at a frequency where double photon absorption can occur. At high lasing powers such absorption is more probable and so saturation sets in. There does appear to be an output power limit of a few watts set by this process, which restricts the effectiveness of the divalent rare earths.

Table 2. The divalent rare earths

Impurity ion	Host lattice	Mode	Temperature °K	Frequency	Threshold
Sm^{2+} [9]	CaF_2	Pulsed	20	14,100	0.01 joule
Tm^{2+} [10]	CaF_2	CW	4	8,620	600W
			27		1 KW
Dy^{2+} [11]	CaF_2	CW	77	4,325	600W
			26		120W

Gas lasers

Mention has already been made of the differences between the energy levels of an ion in the free state and in a crystalline solid, and they are briefly summarized here. In gases, absorption bands are very weak and metastable lifetimes short, usually of the order of a microsecond. The effect of incorporation into a lattice field is to modify the selection rules governing transitions, in such a way that some transition probabilities are greatly increased leading to relatively broad pump bands, while some are reduced leading to long lifetime metastable levels.

These modifications apply so long as the energy difference between the levels in question is many times greater than the energy of the highest lattice vibrational process, usually involving two or more phonons. As the energy of most three-phonon processes is around 1000 cm^{-1}, laser action involving energies less than 3000 cm^{-1} is very unlikely. However, in gases no such restriction applies, and as a result the number of gaseous laser emission lines is so enormous as to be nearly impossible to catalogue; they extend from 3000 angstroms to 337 microns and beyond. It is inevitable that, with the exploitation of more atomic atoms, of gaseous ions of differing excitation states, and of the whole range of molecular interactions, this catalogue of lines will be extended even further.

From this list of emission lines three laser systems stand out as of supreme importance. They are the helium-neon, the ionized argon, and the carbon dioxide systems; the first is an atomic system and the others molecular. They typify the three most prominent types of gas laser and we shall use them as examples; but first, a description of pumping techniques and laser action in a gas.

Pumping a gas laser

Because of the low oscillator strength of the transitions in a gas, and because of the low gas pressure which has to be used, it is in only four cases that optical pumping has been used. A well-known case is in the pumping of caesium vapour, where the transition for excitation into a 'pump level' coincided with a strong emission line in the mercury spectrum.

Three other techniques are available, and apply separately to the three lasers we shall describe. They are by resonant atom-atom collisions, as Javan demonstrated; by electron impact, as in the argon laser;[15] and by molecular dissociation, as in the carbon monoxide and carbon dioxide lasers.[16]

Because of the low density of the gas used, it follows that in many instances the population inversion will be low, and the gain per unit length will be low. In the helium-neon system at 6328 angstroms, the gain is 1.06 per metre. It is essential to keep the losses down to a minimum by the use of high-Q confocal Fabry-Perot resonators, using multi-layer dielectric mirrors having reflectivities of 99.8 per cent. Nevertheless it is often necessary to use long resonators, from 15 cm to 68 metres in length, depending on the gain which can be achieved. Normally the reflectors are outside the gas tube in order to avoid damage to the mirrors by ion bombardment. So it is necessary to terminate the gas tube by low reflectivity flasks set at the Brewster angle to give minimum reflectivity for one plane of polarization.

Typical gas laser systems are sketched in Fig. 10, and shown in Fig. 60. The linewidths of a gaseous atom are broadened to about 1000 Mc/s or 0.2 cm^{-1} by the Doppler effect, owing to the thermal motion within the resonator. So there are usually several cavity modes lying within the fluorescent linewidth and, as with a solid-state laser, considerable care and skill is needed to excite a single axial mode and achieve high power operation within that mode.

Because of the short fluorescent lifetimes of a gaseous atom, pulsed operation has to be restricted to pulses lasting no more than a few microseconds. As ionization of a gas within such a short time is difficult, only relatively low pulse powers have been achieved at low efficiency. In atomic systems, pulsed powers of the order of 1 kW have been obtained. Nevertheless because of the high optical quality of a gas laser compared with its solid-state counterpart, the output beam divergence is close to that set by the theoretical diffraction limits, and such devices may have useful applications.

The helium-neon laser

Neon is well-known for its fluorescent properties and it is not surprising that it should find use as the first gas in which laser action was found. However, as shown in Fig. 9, there are many energy levels in neon. If ions are excited by either a d.c. or a radio-frequency discharge by being accelerated in the electric field, then the population of higher metastable levels such as 2s and 3s will be difficult.

This problem was overcome by the use of a mixture of helium and neon gases, where the helium plays the same role as the coactivating ion plays in resonant transfer in a solid. The first excited state of helium is 2^{3s} at 19.81 cV, which is coincident in energy with the 2s level of neon. Thus through atom-atom collisions it is possible for the helium atom in its excited state to transfer energy directly into one of the metastable states of neon and so produce population inversion. Decay from the 2p levels to the metastable 1s level in a much shorter time than the spontaneous decay time; hence the conditions for population inversion and laser action are fulfilled.

Some direct excitation of neon atoms occurs, and this tends to reduce the population inversion ratio as it provides less discriminant population of all levels. For this reason the mean density is kept well below that of the helium. The 1s level is metastable and so after a time some population build-up occurs in this level. As this build-up occurs, the probability of re-excitation increases, a process known as *radiation trapping*. Ions decay to the ground state from the 1s metastable level only by diffusion to the walls; otherwise a 'bottleneck' occurs. For this reason the tube diameter has to be limited.

The helium-neon laser is now a standard laboratory tool. It appears to be limited to a maximum output power in the region of 50 milliwatts and, until a satisfactory method of overcoming the 'bottlenecking' is found, is unlikely to be increased. A list of the more prominent helium-neon emission lines is given in Table 3.[17, 18]

Table 3. Observed transitions in the helium-neon laser

Wavelength (microns)	Transitions
0.6328	$3S_2-2p_4$
1.1522	$2S_2-2p_4$
3.39	$3S-2p$

The argon ion laser

Laser action, both pulsed and continuous has been observed in singly ionized rare gases; of which the most useful would appear to be ionized argon. Such lasers require high charged particle densities, since the laser transitions are associated with excited states; typical electron densities are in the region of 10^{13} per cu. cm.[19, 20] In order

41

that the d.c. discharge current is of reasonable proportions it is necessary to use small-bore quartz tubing. Discharge currents up to 10 amp can be achieved using heavy-duty, oxide-coated cathodes. The optimum argon pressure is found to be around 0.5 torr.

Several emission lines are found in such a laser, and these are listed in Table 4. By incorporating a high-resolution prism within the resonator, some frequency selection can be achieved. Just above the threshold the output power stays on I^6 relationship changing to on I^4 relationship at high power levels.

Table 4. Emission level of ionized argon

Wavelength (angstroms)	Level design used	Gain
4545	$4P^2P^0_{3/2} \rightarrow 4s^2P_{3/2}$	< 15%
4579	$4P^2S^0_{1/2} \rightarrow 4s^2P_{1/2}$	
4658	$4P^2p^0_{1/2} \rightarrow 2P_{3/2}$	
4727	$4P^2D^0_{3/3} \rightarrow 4s^2P_{3/2}$	
4765	$4P^2p^0_{3/2} \rightarrow 4s^2P_{1/2}$	
4879	$4P^4D^0_{1/2} \rightarrow 4s^2P_{3/2}$	< 15%
4965	$4P^2D^0_{1/2} \rightarrow 4s^2P_{1/2}$	
5017	$4P^2F^0_{5/2} \rightarrow 4s^2P_{3/2}$	
5145	$4P^4D_{5/2} \rightarrow 4sP_{3/2}$	< 10%
5287	$4P^4D^0_{3/2} \rightarrow 4s^2P_{1/2}$	

By increasing the current, the overall efficiency has been increased and powers in excess of 1 watt have been obtained. Nevertheless the argon ion laser is still a device of low efficiency and of relatively short life.

The carbon dioxide laser

The third energy level scheme which can be exploited in a gas consists of the rotational-vibrational bands of a molecule. Such bands exist throughout the electromagnetic spectrum, in both the visible and infrared regions, and allow considerable scope for laser action. Each band consists of a large number of individual levels separated by a few wave numbers, and so a complex of laser emission lines is to be expected. The most interesting gas laser so far exploits the P-branch rotational transitions which occur in carbon dioxide gas around 9.4 and 10.4 microns.[21, 22]

A discharge is produced in a tube an inch in diameter and 5 metres long by d.c. excitation, using a gas pressure of around 0.2 torr.

Alkali halide Brewster windows are used in the tube, and near confocal silicon mirrors coated with aluminium form the resonant cavity. The $001°$ level is populated either by direct electron excitation, or by radiationless transitions from upper excited levels; or, as seems most likely, by resonant transfer from other molecular levels owing to added impurities such as nitrogen or helium.

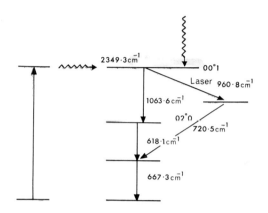

Figure 20 Energy level diagram for the carbon dioxide laser.

Laser action takes place either to the $02°0$ level at 1039.39 cm^{-1}, P(28) this being the strongest of seven evenly spaced P branches ranging from P(22) to P(34) or to the 100-degree level at 940.52 cm^{-1} (P24), as shown in Fig. 20. The decay of the laser output consists of two distinct exponentials, having time constants of 50 and 150 microseconds, believed to be due to the cascading and recombination processes leading to the population of the upper level.

One possible sequence of events is as follows:

$$CO_2 + (e + \text{k.e.}) \rightarrow CO^* + O + e$$
$$CO(X^1\Sigma^+) + O(^3P) \rightarrow CO_2^* \rightarrow CO_2^* (^1B)$$
$$CO_2^{**} (^1B) \rightarrow CO_2 (^1\Sigma^+) + h\nu$$

The various wavelengths which have been observed to lase are in reasonable agreement with absorption measurements made previously. The latter are likely to be in error due to collisions at high pressures and so the laser emission measurements are, most probably, the more accurate. By the use of resonant transfer processes, the overall efficiency of the carbon dioxide laser has been increased up to nearly 14 per cent, and power outputs of 180n watts have been reported.

This great advance in laser technology has come about through a study of resonant transfer processes in gases. A mixture of helium-nitrogen and carbon dioxide is used with $P_{\text{He}} = 7$ torr, $P_{\text{nz}} = 1.2$, $P_{\text{co}2} = 0.33$. It is believed that the following reaction occurs:

$$He^*(2^3S_1) + 2N_2 \rightarrow He + 4N - \Delta E$$

where $\Delta E < 0.1$ eV

The atomic nitrogen so formed by collisional excitation with excited helium recombines to form molecular nitrogen having large energies This energy decays and excites the carbon dioxide molecules into $00^\circ1$ levels, leading to subsequent laser action.

4

SEMICONDUCTOR LASERS

DR CYRIL HILSUM
Royal Radar Establishment, Malvern

In Chapter 3 Dr Goodwin has described the two forms of laser which were discovered first. The great interest which was aroused by their discovery attracted many scientists to this field, and among them were a number of semiconductor physicists. They were not drawn in simply by the philosophy that everything can be done better by semiconductors, although this did, perhaps, colour their approach. But they could see that if a semiconductor laser could be made it would have a number of advantages over the other types.

It had already been shown that an electric current passing through a semiconductor could be converted into infrared radiation with high efficiency, and that this radiation could be modulated at high speed simply by switching the current on and off. The theoretical work that laid the foundations was completed during 1961, and throughout 1962 a number of laboratories tried to make the device. In the early months of that year, Russian workers at the Joffe laboratories in Leningrad were very near to success, but they were held up by various difficulties.[23] By mid-1962 it became clear that a semiconductor laser was feasible, and the pace of the research increased. It was amid considerable excitement that R. N. Hall and his co-workers at the General Electric Research Laboratories made the first semiconductor laser towards the end of September 1962,[24] just three or four days before independent work by M. Nathan at the IBM Research Laboratory was also successful.[25] Before the end of the year three other laboratories — two American and one British — had made working semiconductor lasers;[26] and a few weeks later the Russian device operated.[27] All these lasers were basically similar, consisting of a junction diode made from the semiconducting compound, gallium arsenide.

Radiation emission from semiconductors

There are two possible ways in which electricity can be conducted through a semiconductor. The type of conductivity is determined by the nature of the impurities in the material.

If a semiconductor like silicon is prepared with a small amount of phosphorus in it, there will be excess electrons available for conduction, because each phosphorus atom carries five valence electrons, one more than the silicon atom it replaces. These conduction electrons are negatively charged, so the semiconductor is said to be n-type. If the impurity in the crystal is not phosphorus, but indium, there will be a shortage of valence electrons, because each indium atom carries only three. For each indium atom there will be one electron vacancy. Conduction can now take place by the valence electrons moving into these vacancies, or 'holes'. The holes act as i they were charged positively, and the crystal is, in this case, said to be p-type.

Many other semiconductors can be prepared in either the p-type or n-type form, but the impurities required depend on the particular semiconductor. For a compound like gallium arsenide, tellurium gives excess electrons and makes the crystal n-type, and zinc makes it p-type.

A crystal can also be prepared with an impurity concentration gradient along it, with one part p-type and the other n-type. The transition region is called a p-n junction. It acts as a rectifier of electric current, passing electricity easily only when the p-region is biased positively. Holes are then injected from the p-region into the n-region, and electrons from the n-region into the p-region.

The foreign carriers cannot live for long once they have been injected, and they soon recombine with carriers of the opposite charge. Some energy must then be given up, for each conduction electron carries with it the energy which was supplied to release it from its parent atom. The energy released can take the form either of heat or light. In some semiconductors, notably silicon and germanium, the recombination energy is given up mostly as heat, and these materials are useless for semiconductor lasers. In other materials, such as gallium arsenide, most of the energy appears as light.

The wavelength at which this light is emitted is a characteristic of the particular semiconductor. It depends on the energy required to free a valence electron, and it is called the 'activation energy'. Gallium arsenide has an activation energy of 1.4 electron volts, and photons with this energy have a wavelength of 9000 angstroms; that is, in the near-infrared part of the spectrum.

We see then that when current is passed through a p-n junction of gallium arsenide, the junction will emit infrared radiation. However, this is not sufficient to give us a semiconductor laser. We must also provide means for this radiation to be amplified.

Light amplification in semiconductors

In general, when light of a suitable wavelength falls upon a semiconductor, it will be absorbed. The energy is passed to some of the valence electrons, which are then freed from the atoms to which they are bound. There is a second process which can happen, although it is rather unlikely. An incident photon might persuade a conduction electron to recombine with a hole, giving up its recombination energy as an additional photon, which is then identical in all respects to the original photon (Fig. 21).

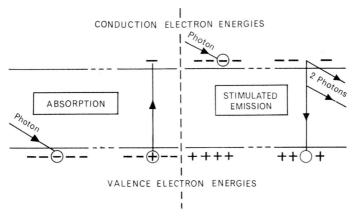

Figure 21 Energy diagram illustrating absorption and stimulated emission in a semiconductor.

This effect, stimulated emission, is infrequent because it can occur with high probability only when there are simultaneously present a large number of free electrons and a large number of holes. This does not happen in thermal equilibrium, and so the incident radiation is absorbed. But the requirements for stimulated emission are met in the narrow region near a forward-biased *p-n* junction — provided that the current density is high.

Radiation travelling in this region is not absorbed, but amplified. The amplification will be repeated if the photons continue to travel near to the junction, but they can only do this if the junction is extremely flat, and if the original photon was travelling exactly in the plane of the junction. Otherwise the radiation will soon leave the 'active' amplifying region and become absorbed.

The original photon which gives rise to the stimulated emission need not come from outside the crystal. It can just as well be some recombination radiation emitted by the junction itself. But only that part of the radiation which is emitted in the plane of the junction is amplified.

One more thing is needed for a semiconductor laser: an optical resonator containing the *p-n* junction. This is to make the amplified

47

radiation travel to and fro, always remaining within the active junction region. It is best constructed by cutting the crystal so that two end faces are exactly perpendicular to the junction, and parallel to one another. The reflecting properties of these ends will be satisfactory without any special coating, because most semiconductors have a high refractive index, and the reflection at an air-semiconductor interface is therefore high.

Figure 22 Semiconductor laser, comprising a cube of gallium arsenide sandwiched between two connectors.

So the semiconductor laser takes the form of a rectangular slab of semiconductor held between two metal connectors, which conduct the electricity in, and conduct the excess heat away (Fig. 22). The junction lies parallel to the metal-semiconductor interfaces, a few microns away from one interface, and has been prepared so that it is extremely flat. Two end faces are optically polished or cleaved parallel to each other and perpendicular to the junction; the other two surfaces are roughened. The dimensions of the slab are typically 100 microns by 200 microns, with a thickness of 100 microns. It is clearly a much smaller device than the lasers described in Chapter 3 (see Fig. 23).

Inverted populations in semiconductors

We have discussed the operation of a semiconductor laser in a general way, without mentioning the energy levels involved in the processes. It is proper that we should now briefly treat this topic, because the principles of operation are not quite the same as for the gas laser and the optically pumped laser.

The energy values which are available to electrons in a semiconductor lie in two groups. In each group the energy states are so close together that they overlap, and coalesce into an energy band. These two energy bands are separated by an energy gap which is called the

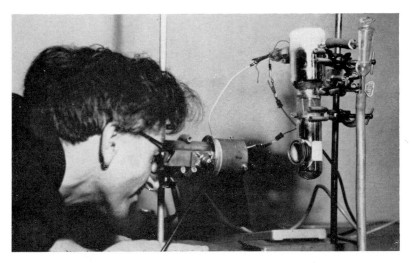

Figure 23 Dr Cyril Hilsum examines the infrared radiation from a gallium arsenide laser with an image converter. (*Courtesy, Services Electronics Research Laboratory.*)

'forbidden gap'. This is the same as the activation energy of the semiconductor.

The conduction electrons have energy values near the bottom of the upper band. The valence electrons have energies within the lower band, and the vacancies, or holes, have energies near the top of this band. Recombination takes place across the forbidden gap, an electron at the bottom of the conduction band recombining with a hole at the top of the valence band.

This is in contrast with the transition processes in the other lasers, where isolated energy levels are involved. In thermal equilibrium the population of electrons and holes in the two bands can be described by simple mathematical functions which bring in the temperature of the crystal. When we inject extra carriers into the semiconductor the populations in the two bands are quite differently distributed from those in thermal equilibrium, but they can still be described by the same mathematical function. The temperature we would need to use now would not be the temperature of the crystal, but some artificial temperature. At very high injected currents, when the probability of light absorption is low and that of stimulated emission is high (see Fig. 24), the temperature needed to describe the distribution is a negative temperature.

We have now an inverted population, just as for stimulated emission in other types of laser, but now the population is contained in energy bands, not in isolated levels. It is easier to invert the population if the temperature of the crystal is low, and early semiconductor

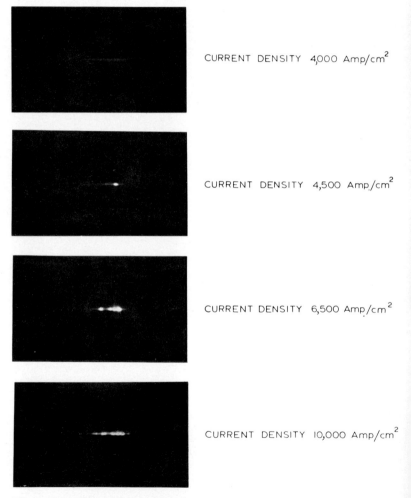

CURRENT DENSITY 4,000 Amp/cm^2

CURRENT DENSITY 4,500 Amp/cm^2

CURRENT DENSITY 6,500 Amp/cm^2

CURRENT DENSITY 10,000 Amp/cm^2

Figure 24 Infrared photographs of a semiconductor laser junction, showing the onset of laser action.

lasers were operated at 77°K (liquid nitrogen temperature) or lower. Recent progress has led to room-temperature operations in some cases.

Properties of semiconductor lasers

The first semiconductor laser was made from gallium arsenide, but now a number of materials have been used. The complete list is given in Table 5, with the wavelength of the radiation emitted. This wavelength is determined by the energy gap of the semiconductor and changes slightly with temperature. The values given are for a temperature of 77°K.

Table 5. Materials for semiconductor lasers

Material	Emitted Wavelength (microns)
GaAs	0.85
InP	0.90
GaSb	1.6
InAs	3.2
InSb	5.3
PbTe	6.5 (4.2°K)
PbSe	8.5 (4.2°K)
GaAs–GaP alloys	0.65–0.9
InAs–InP ,,	0.9–3.2
GaAs–InAs ,,	0.85–3.2

It is possible to make alloys from some pairs of materials, and then the energy gap is a function of the particular composition used for the alloy. It is thus possible to produce any wavelength between the extremes given by the two materials; for example, gallium arsenide emits at 0.85 microns and indium arsenide at 3.2 microns. An alloy of GaAs and InAs will emit somewhere between these two wavelengths, depending on the relative amounts of GaAs and InAs in the alloy.

The radiation emitted by a semiconductor laser is spread over a range of wavelengths that is large compared with the gas laser. The precise spread depends on the operating conditions. In the first place the current densities required for laser action are large, so that the excitation must usually take the form of current pulses. The temperature of the crystal will rise during the pulses, so the wavelength emitted will also change. Further, the different parts of the junction may emit at slightly different wavelengths, because the energy transition is not precisely defined. Small, cooled lasers may be operated continuous-wave, and then can give a line width as narrow as 50 megacycles. More normal operation gives line widths of approximately 1 angstrom; and if the device is driven well above threshold, a value of 20 angstroms is not uncommon.

A second 'unlaser-like' property is the beam spread. The active region of the junction is only a micron or two wide. The emitted light is, therefore, diffracted as though it is emerging from a narrow slit, and it spreads over an angle of 10 degrees. In the plane of the junction there is little diffraction but the spread is still rarely less than 2 degrees. The semiconductor laser is, therefore, not noteworthy on either of these counts. Where it does score is in its conversion efficiency, and in its ease and speed of modulation.

The semiconductor laser is the most efficient device we have for converting electricity into radiation. Almost half of the electrons injected into the crystal as electric current give rise to emergent photons. The conversion efficiency at the junction is near 100 per cent, but some of the photons produced are absorbed. Usually the efficiency gets less as the temperature is raised above $77°K$, but in some lasers quite good efficiency is obtained even at room temperature.

The speed of the laser is high. The spontaneous recombination lifetime is near 10^{-9} second (1 nanosecond), but the stimulated lifetime is an order of magnitude less. The radiation can, therefore, be switched on and off very rapidly simply by modulating the drive current. The highest modulation speed recorded is 11 gigacycles, but this need not be an absolute limit.

Though its efficiency is high, the power output is rather low, because the devices are so small. Generally the threshold current density needed for stimulated emission is about 1000 amp per sq. cm at $77°K$. An average laser will have a cross-sectional area less than 1 sq. mm, and the output at threshold will be about 5 watts peak. Lasers driven well above threshold have given peak outputs near 100 watts, but these cannot be sustained for long pulses because the laser heats up so much.

Lasers can be made with a longer active region, and this to some extent lowers the threshold current. But special care must be taken for lengths greater than 1 mm to ensure that the junction is flat and that losses due to crystal non-uniformities do not counterbalance the potential gains. Obviously it is more difficult to take the excess heat away from the larger lasers, and a number of special devices have been developed which incorporate efficient heat sinks. A laser 1 cm long, made with care from high-quality gallium arsenide, and fitted with sapphire and copper heat sinks, has given out 15 watts of radiation, operating continuous-wave at $4°K$. Smaller devices have worked continuously at $77°K$, with an output of one or two watts.

It would seem possible in principle to make the laser area greater by increasing the width. This has not proved successful because most lasers operate in 'filaments' which have little interaction with each other. The more 'filaments' there are, the broader the emitted spectrum. One can do better by mounting small lasers side by side, since each component can be tested before assembly. Moreover, since the laser is a low-voltage, high-current device, it is more convenient to drive the larger area with the various component diodes in series, thus reducing the current requirements.

Laser arrays have been constructed which exploit these points. One operating system uses ten lasers mounted one above the other, connected electrically in series. Each laser is equipped with a small cylindrical lens, and the optics are completed with one large cylindrical lens. With the lasers cooled to 77°K the peak output is near a kilowatt, and the mean output about 10 watts. Clearly the emitted radiation is not coherent, but the array is used just as a bright source.

For most practical applications, cooling to 77°K is a nuisance, and considerable effort has been directed to obtaining room-temperature operation. The original design of laser did work at room temperature, but the threshold current density increased rapidly with temperatures above 77°K, and was commonly between 100,000 and a million amp per sq. cm at 300°K. Special drive circuits have been developed which can give these currents in short pulses.

But a partial solution to the problem has come from another direction — from modification of the laser's construction. In the original devices the junction was formed as in most semiconductor devices, by gaseous diffusion of the p-type impurity into an n-type crystal. The newer method is to grow the p-type material from a liquid solution on top of the n-type crystal. This has two advantages. The new part of the crystal grows along the original crystal planes, and the junction is, therefore, extremely flat. This improves the efficiency and reduces the threshold current at all temperatures. Secondly, the concentration of impurities in the junction region can be kept very high for solution growth. This has little effect at the lower temperatures, but gives relatively low threshold currents at temperatures above 150°K. Threshold current densities of 10,000 amp per sq. cm at 300°K are probably now within reach.

A number of workers have made laser systems which give several watts of peak at room temperature, and since simple transistor power supplies can be used the whole system is extremely compact.

Although the only practical semiconductor lasers rely on carrier injection from an electric current, it is possible to obtain stimulated emission in these materials in two other ways. First an inverted population can be achieved by optical pumping, generally using another semiconductor laser as the pump, or by bombarding the crystal with a high-energy electron beam. Several materials have been investigated in this way and the standard crystals such as gallium arsenide, indium arsenide and indium antimonide have shown laser action. It is more interesting to note that electron bombardment experiments on cadmium sulphide and gallium selenide have also been successful. We do not yet know how to make $p-n$ junctions in these materials, and so have been unable to make junction lasers from them. Both cadmium sulphide and gallium selenide emit yellow radiation. The equipment required for electron bombardment is rather complex, and cooling to at least $77\,^{\circ}$K is needed.

The characteristics of semiconductor lasers make them suitable for use where high coherence and narrow beam divergence are not necessary. The high speed and ease of modulation points to use in communication systems, and initial results of television transmission over paths of 30 miles are very encouraging. For optical radar the semiconductor laser will never give ranges as long as the ruby laser, because the peak power is so low, but when ranges of only a few miles are satisfactory, and high repetition rate is required, the semiconductor device will be more suitable. A gallium arsenide laser altimeter has already been operated with success, and used for calibrating radio altimeters at low altitudes.

The high efficiency and brightness of this laser makes it attractive simply as a bright lamp, but here we must await more development at visible wavelengths. The success of electron bombardment excitation opens this field, but it may be some years before it can be exploited. A directional beam of high intensity and efficiency would clearly be useful on airfields and in lighthouses.

The compactness of this laser may lead to its use as the optical element in 'opto-electronic' systems. Fortunately, the silicon photocell has high sensitivity at wavelengths where gallium arsenide lasers emit radiation, and the simple laser-detector combination should find widespread use in instrumentation. The application of opto-electronics to computers is still under consideration, but if practical systems are developed the semiconductor laser would clearly make a suitable source of light.

We should, however, remember that the semiconductor laser is the youngest member of the family, and it has not changed in its basic form since its invention. Considerable thought is now going into modifications of this form, and we may well find that in a few years' time the practical laser bears only a slight resemblance to the device we have today.

5

HOLOGRAPHY BY LASER LIGHT*

PROFESSOR DENNIS GABOR, F.R.S.

Department of Electrical Engineering, Imperial College, London

The idea of light as a wave motion has been familiar to us since our schooldays. If we allow ourselves a moment of naïve wonderment, we may realize that this apparently simple idea is an extraordinary achievement of the human mind. All our instruments, the eye, the photographic plate, the photocell measure only light energies. The laws of the propagation of light energy are so complicated that until ten years ago we had no adequate mathematical description of it. The intuition that light energy was the square of something else which obeyed simple laws of superposition was such a stroke of genius that I am convinced it would have been beyond the gigantic ability of Christian Huygens, had it not been suggested by water and sound waves.

The recognition that colour corresponds to wavelength came much later, by the work of Thomas Young and Augustin Fresnel. The formulation that light 'consists' of regular vibrations is open to several objections. It is associated with the widespread misconception that a prism or grating, by 'breaking up' light into a spectrum of colours, gives a complete analysis — what physicists call a Fourier analysis — of the light. Eddington's remark that 'if a physicist wants to Fourier-analyse a process, he is free to do it', is not quite correct. What the physicist produces with a prism or a grating is not a complete Fourier analysis but a 'periodogram'; it gives the energies at each wavelength, but leaves the phases — the occurrence in space and time of the peaks and troughs of the waves — entirely unknown. In fact the 'temporal phase' of light from conventional sources is strictly non-observable. What is observable is only the 'spatial phase' — the relation in space of waves of the same wavelength. But even this remains rather non-physical: however carefully the physicist sieves out the same wavelength from two different sources, he can never bring them to interfere observably with one another; a light source interferes only with itself. To put this more exactly, only

*Most of this chapter originally appeared in *New Scientist* (reference 10).

a very small region of a single light source is self-consistent in phase, or 'coherent'; a region so small that its details cannot be resolved in the given optical arrangement because of the finite wavelength of light. All this is changed by the invention of the laser, the very unconventional source whose light is coherent over a large volume and long periods.

Birth of holography

I first became interested in the problems which ultimately led to holography a long time ago, at the age of seventeen, when I had learned about Huygens' principle of the propagation of wavefronts, and read Abbe's theory of the microscope. I asked myself a question: 'When we take a photograph, the image appears in the plane of the plate. But by Huygens' principle the information which goes into the image must be there in every plane before the plate, also in the plane before the lens. How can it be there in that uniform whiteness? Why can we not extract it?' White light, of course, is a jumble, but could we not do it with light of one wavelength?

I could give a complete answer to my own question only many years later, in 1955, in the 'matrix theory of light propagation', which half a year later was also discovered, quite independently, by the young Japanese mathematician Hideya Gamo. Briefly stated, the somewhat discouraging answer is as follows: If an optical system can resolve N elements or 'picture points' of an image, the complete description of a monochromatic but incoherent light-field requires $N \times N$ data.

If the light is multi-coloured, the description is even more complicated. Every one of these data is of the nature of an energy; it is physically measurable, but evidently the work of collecting $N \times N$ data by suitably contrived experiments and then extracting from them the N data of the image is prohibitive. It is much better and simpler to use a lens!

However, some years previously I had found that, if the illumination is coherent, we might well dispense with a lens. For a full discussion of coherence I must refer the reader to the excellent textbook by Born and Wolf.[28] For the present it will be sufficient to give a practical rule. Light has sufficient coherence for an image with $N = n \times n$ 'picture points' if it is capable of giving n well distinguishable interference fringes across the image, in any direction. The concept of coherence in terms of the visibility of interference fringes was first understood and ingeniously utilized by A. A. Michelson, and later put into mathematical form by van Cittert and Zernike. When this criterion is satisfied, we can deal with the light as if it were a strictly regular vibration, with fully defined amplitude and phase in every point of interest. Thus, instead of the $N \times N$ data which characterize the general light-field, we have now only 2N; N amplitudes and N phases, two for every picture point instead of N. Dispensing with a lens no longer appears so hopeless.

The problem which had interested me as a high-school boy came to my attention again in 1947 via electron microscopy. At that time it was well known that electron lenses could never be made perfect, and their aberrations prevented the microscopist from attaining a discrimination power sufficient for revealing individual atoms. Perhaps, I thought, we could get over this hurdle if we took an imperfect picture with an electron lens, but one which nevertheless contained the full information, though in a garbled form, and corrected it by means of a light-optical process.

I was encouraged and inspired by W. L. Bragg's 'X-ray microscope', in which the position of the atoms in a crystal could be reconstructed by optical means from a diffraction diagram obtained with X-rays. But this instrument worked only if the phase was known and was constant — which is the case only in certain rather exceptional crystals when viewed along a crystal axis. How could we obtain the phases in an unknown, irregular object?

It was a fairly obvious idea to get a grip on the phases by superimposing a known and preferably simple coherent wave on the diffraction pattern. The phases might then reveal themselves, by increasing the intensity where they happened to coincide with the phase of the 'coherent background', and decreasing it where they were in opposition.

This simple idea worked out even better than one might have expected at first sight. The proof is not difficult. The amplitude of light at any point of the photographic plate is the sum of two simple harmonic terms (Fig. 25), one representing the amplitude and phase of the coherent wave issuing from the object, the other the amplitude and phase of the coherent background. The photographic plate records the intensity of the light (the square of the amplitude), but

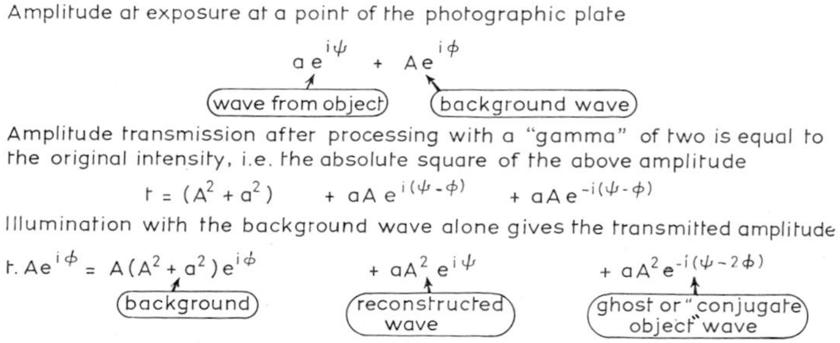

Amplitude at exposure at a point of the photographic plate

$$a e^{i\psi} \quad + \quad A e^{i\phi}$$

(wave from object) (background wave)

Amplitude transmission after processing with a "gamma" of two is equal to the original intensity, i.e. the absolute square of the above amplitude

$$t = (A^2 + a^2) \quad + aA e^{i(\psi-\phi)} \quad + aA e^{-i(\psi-\phi)}$$

Illumination with the background wave alone gives the transmitted amplitude

$$t. A e^{i\phi} = A(A^2 + a^2)e^{i\phi} \quad + aA^2 e^{i\psi} \quad + aA^2 e^{-i(\psi-2\phi)}$$

(background) (reconstructed wave) (ghost or "conjugate object" wave)

Figure 25 Mathematical basis of wavefront reconstruction or 'holography'.

one can arrange to develop and print the plate as a transparency such that the resulting intensity of transmission at any point is proportional to the square of the intensity at exposure. Now illuminate this transparency with the coherent background alone: the transmitted amplitude is proportional to the intensity of the original exposure. As the last equation in Fig. 25 shows, it turns out that the resulting amplitude is made up of three terms: one represents the illuminating wave; one is the reconstructed wave representing the object (which is what we are after); and the third is a ghost. But, if the reconstructed wave is the same as the original wave in one plane it will be, by Huygens' principle, the same as the original in all planes.

Wavefront reconstruction

Hence, we have completely reconstructed the wave which issued from the original object, in three dimensions. It is true that the reconstructed wave is now mixed up with the illuminating wave and with the third, unwanted wave, which appears to issue from a 'conjugate object'. Their complete separation is a rather long story, but the main object appeared to be achieved. By using a coherent electron beam it must be possible to fix the original wavefront on a photographic plate, and to produce the equivalent of a good electron lens by unscrambling the picture with a correcting light optical system.

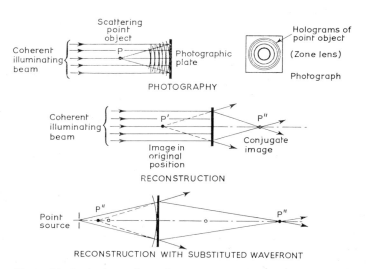

Figure 26 Beginnings of wavefront reconstruction by 'in-line' holography, in 1947. The wavefront used in the reconstruction need not be the same, nor need it have the same wavelength, as that used in taking the hologram. The two reconstructed objects are optical conjugates with respect to the reconstructive wavefront, considered as a spherical mirror.

I called this method 'wavefront reconstruction', and for the photograph which was produced by the joint action of the wave diffracted by the object and by the coherent background I introduced the name 'hologram', from the Greek word *holos* which means 'the whole', because it contained the whole information on amplitudes and phases.

In 1947–48, with my collaborator I. Williams, I carried out what we considered as 'optical-model experiments' in preparation of the electron-optical programme in the Research Laboratory of British Thomson-Houston, Rugby. Our experimental set-up was very simple. The only way of obtaining coherent light in those days before the laser was to take a small pinhole of a few microns in diameter, and to illuminate it with a reasonably monochromatic source, such as one line of a mercury lamp.

We took transparent objects, such as microfilms of text, and illuminated them through a pinhole. As Fig. 26 shows, the photographic plate was put behind the pinhole, at some distance, and at every point it recorded the sum of the coherent background and of the beam diffracted by the object.

Thus in this simplest of arrangements the illuminating beam and the coherent background were one and the same. It would not have been much good to look for more complicated interferometric set-ups, first because the coherence available at that time was good enough only for this simple 'in-line' arrangement, and secondly, because the optical experiment was a model for the electron microscope applica-

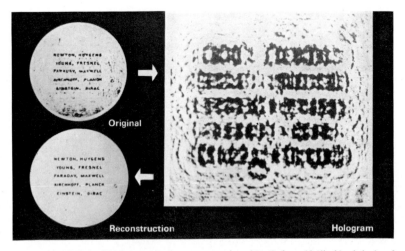

Figure 27 Original hologram and reconstruction (*D. Gabor, 1948*). (A pinhole of 3 microns was used 10 mm from the object, with the plate 180 mm behind. Wavelength of light was 0.4358 microns.)

tions, and at that time no electron-optical beam splitters were known. (Since that time a very ingenious one has been invented by G. Mollenstedt.) With the simple 'in-line' method we achieved the results illustrated in Fig. 27. It was enough to encourage an attack on the electron-microscope problem.

As it turned out, the electron-microscopic application of the idea fizzled out after a few years, in spite of considerable efforts devoted to it by M. E. Haine, J. Dyson and T. Mulvey in the AEI Research Laboratory, Aldermaston, because it turned out that at that time the electron microscope had not yet reached its 'optical' limit. In retrospect, the main achievement of this project was that it led to a thorough understanding of the electron microscope, and to its improvement on 'classical' lines. Discrimination was limited not so much by the imperfection of the electron lenses as by mechanical vibration, magnetic disturbances and, worst of all, by the growth of the microscopic object by 'contamination' during the time of the exposure.

In the meantime, all these disturbances have been eliminated by patient work, and the resolving power of electron microscopic objectives has been also improved, from perhaps 12 angstroms in 1948 to about 3.8 angstroms in 1964. The time may now have come when the optical post-correction of electron micrographs could achieve 1.5–2 angstroms, and so resolve atomic lattices themselves. The spirited attack of Dr Haine and his collaborators came about fifteen years too early.

Laser holograms

On the other hand, the optical experiments had an unexpected revival about twelve years later with the invention of the laser, the new abundant source of coherent light. The new age in holography started

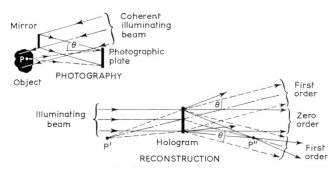

Figure 28 First improvement in wavefront reconstruction. Skew illumination in photography, perpendicular in reconstruction. (*E. N. Leith and J. Upatnieks, 1963.*)

with a paper by Emmett N. Leith and Juris Upatnieks of the University of Michigan, in December 1963.[29] They introduced a great improvement by separating the illuminating beam and the coherent background, which they call 'reference beam' and which in their arrangement (Fig. 28) had a skew incidence on the photographic plate. Fig. 29 shows a strongly magnified portion of one of their holograms, and Fig. 30 one of their first reconstructions.

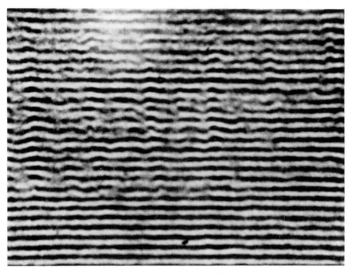

Figure 29   Hologram with laser light and skew reference beam (*Leith and Upatnieks, 1963*).

The hologram is now entirely unlike the original and appears as a slightly distorted system of parallel interference fringes. One can understand this by thinking of the object (a photograph) as featureless, and producing a plane wave. This plane wave will interfere with the reference beam, and would by itself produce a system of regular straight fringes. But the photograph is not, in fact, featureless, so the wave will not be plane, and the fringes will be modulated in amplitude and in position.

In reconstruction, as shown in Fig. 30, the coherent illuminating wave falls perpendicularly on the hologram. If this were a regular grating there would be diffraction only in certain directions: zero order in the direction of the illuminating beam, and two first orders at the sides of it, at equal angles. (If the basic grating pattern is not exactly sinusoidal there will also be diffracted beams of higher order.) As the fringe pattern in the hologram is modulated, the diffracted beams are not simple parallel beams. One contains the

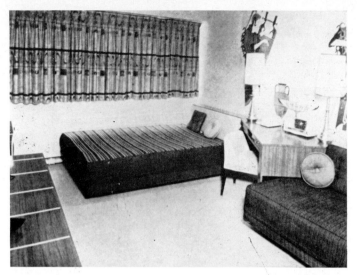

Figure 30 Reconstruction of a photograph from a hologram with laser light and a skew reference beam (*Leith and Upatnieks, 1963.*)

wavefront of the original object, the other the wavefront of its conjugate. The 'conjugate object' which marred the reconstruction in the original 'in-line' method is now separated from the original — not only in position but also in direction.

The results are immensely superior to those which I obtained in 1948, although the theory is fully implied in Fig. 25. This great progress was obtainable only through the superior coherence of laser light. With the high-pressure mercury lamp the chromatic coherence length was about 0.1 mm, sufficient for at most 200 fringes; hence the incidence of the light had to be nearly perpendicular. Even so, the limited spatial coherence with a pinhole, which could not be made so small as to require prohibitively long photographic exposures, reduced the coherence to perhaps 100 fringes. With a helium-neon gas laser one can easily obtain a million fringes. So one can allow a skewing angle of 0.1 radians, or even more.

Professor George W. Stroke and his collaborators in the University of Michigan have since shown that results greatly superior to

Figure 31 Second improvement in wavefront reconstruction. Diffused illumination. (*Leith and Upatnieks, 1964.*)

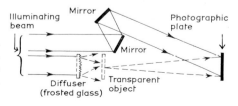

my reconstructions of 1948 can be obtained in my old 'in-line' method, using lasers and certain precautions.[30]

In 1964, Leith and Upatnieks achieved an even more spectacular improvement by introducing diffused illumination of the object,[9] as illustrated in Fig. 31. (The use of diffuse illumination in holography appears to have been first formally suggested by Professor G. W. Stroke in his lecture notes *An Introduction to Optics of Coherent and non-Coherent Electromagnetic Radiations*, University of Michigan, May 1964.) A diffuser, such as frosted glass, does not spoil the coherence of the beam; it merely produces a complicated, rough wavefront. The resulting hologram, shown greatly magnified in Fig. 32, is now even more unlike the original; it looks like random 'noise', because the information on every object point is now spread practically over the whole plate.

Each point of the object now emits a wide-angle beam, and the result is that the whole object can be seen through any point of the

Figure 32 Greatly enlarged portion of a hologram taken by Leith and Upatnieks with the diffused illumination method. This is *not* grain noise, but information spread out in a noise-like fashion over the whole period.

plate. Every square millimetre of the hologram contains information on the whole object, although the definition is poor. Adding all the points of the hologram improves the definition and the signal-to-noise ratio. One great advantage is that one can now see three-dimensional objects through the hologram, without the use of a lens. Three-dimensional images are not of course suitable for reproduction, but the two-dimensional reconstruction of a photograph, shown in Fig. 33 gives an idea of the perfection of modern holography.

Figure 33 Reconstruction of a photograph from a hologram such as in Figure 32. (*Leith and Upatnieks, 1965.*)

A hologram is not merely a three-dimensional record of an object, such as one could obtain with other means. A stereoscopic pair of photographs is not really three-dimensional; it shows the relief of the object only as viewed by two eyes in a certain fixed position, and even then it requires the human brain to 'fuse' corresponding points to obtain a sense of depth. In a hologram one can look at the record of the object — from any point of view so long as the appropriate rays fall inside the plate.

In addition, as a hologram contains a full record of the phases, it can represent also the fully-transparent 'phase objects' — just as if the original object were in position. A convincing proof of this lies in an experiment recently carried out by Professor Stroke and his collaborators.[31] Fig. 34(a) shows the hologram of a pure phase object,

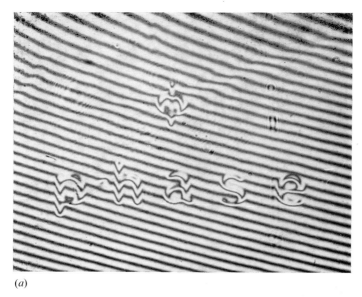

(a)

Figure 34 (a) Hologram of a pure phase object. Relief, invisible to the eye, was obtained by bleaching a fine-grain photographic plate.
(b) Hologram of the hologram shown in (a). The aerial image formed by the first hologram is recorded on a plate, together with the same coherent background. (*Gabor, Stroke, et al., 1965.*)

(b)

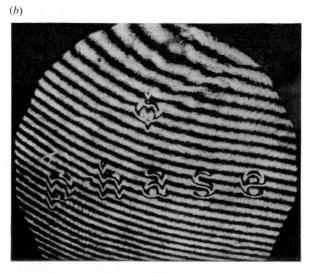

and Fig. 34(b) the hologram of the hologram. That is to say, they have 'taken a picture' of the aerial image formed by the hologram, using a coherent skew background to form the second hologram. The two are identical.

At least 100 laboratories in the United States are now working on holography. Lensless holography has an intrinsic advantage over ordinary photography, because there is no lens which can fully exploit the information capacity of modern fine-grain photographic plates. A plate of 10×10 cm can record about 100 million picture points, while the best lens is capable of only a few million.

The phase-recording property of holograms has already been put to good use, in photographing explosion waves with one giant pulse of a solid-state laser; these can then be explored at leisure in three dimensions. Three-dimensional movies have also been produced, although they can be viewed by only one person at a time.

The interesting property of holograms that they encode information in a 'noise-like' form, spread all over the plate, has been put to good use in the photography of objects with brightnesses which vary in the ratio of, say, 1:10,000. The photographic plate has a range of about 1:100 but, as the light of a small bright area will be spread over the whole area of the plate, the original range can be restored in the reconstruction.

Professor L. J. Cutrona and his associates in the Radar Laboratory of the University of Michigan, have made ingenious applications of

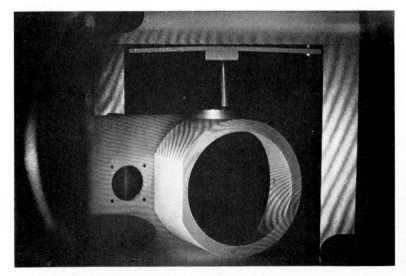

Figure 35 How laser light can reveal the stress patterns in an engineering component. (*Photograph, courtesy University of Michigan.*)

holography to radar pictures. Dr C. A. Burch at the National Physical Laboratory, Teddington, and also K. L. Stetson and R. L. Powell in the University of Michigan have applied holography to the optical testing of surfaces and their deformations. If one takes a hologram of the undeformed surface, and puts it back into its original position, deformations will produce interference fringes, just as if one had a material template (Fig. 35). Character recognition is another promising field of holography in the future. [32]

When I first conceived the idea of holography, eighteen years ago, I had in mind first of all electron microscopy and electron-structure diagrams. I thought also, of course, of X-ray crystallography, but I dismissed it because the intensity of coherent X-rays is about 1000 times less than that of coherent electrons, and their interaction with matter is also about 1000 times weaker. Others, however, did not share my view, and perhaps they were right.

Holography with X-rays is particularly attractive, because we have no X-ray lenses. Soon after my first papers, H. M. A. El-Sum, in his Ph.D thesis at Stanford produced some X-ray images of simple objects by holography. The idea was taken up recently in particular by Professor Stroke and his collaborators, who have done successful spade-work in clearing the ground for X-ray holography by proving that holograms can be produced also with extended sources.

But the most important recent progress in holography is the production of three-dimensional images in natural colours which can be viewed in white light. This was achieved by the co-operation of Pennington and Lin of the Bell Telephone Laboratories, together with Stroke and Labeyrie of the University of Michigan, and it is a combination of the idea of holography with Gabriel Lippmann's method of colour photography (of 1891). An object is illuminated in front of a photographic plate with three lasers — say, red, green and blue — and the reference beams from the same lasers fall on the emulsion from the back. The interference of the two beams going in almost opposite directions produces standing waves, and these produce precipitation of fine silver grains in parallel planes, bisecting the direction of the two beams, and spaced by about one wavelength from one another. When illuminated with ordinary white light these silver layers act as spatial and colour filters: every ray will be seen in the original direction and in the original colours.

It is very likely that this striking invention will soon be exploited, for advertisements and perhaps also for a new type of portrait and the like.

6

THE LASER ON THE BATTLEFIELD

BARRY MILLER

Boston, USA

Like few other major scientific or technological discoveries made during periods of relative world tranquillity, the laser is linked inseparably to military interests. Indeed, in large measure the origins of the laser, the rapidity of its early development, and the excitement it sparked in government and industrial circles all can be traced to an underlying belief in its ultimate applicability to military or weapon systems. Today, nearly seven years after coherent light was first generated, it is apparent that were it not for the military motivation, the laser would hardly be more than a promising albeit exciting scientific invention.

True, the first laser was operated in the privately-owned laboratories of the Hughes Aircraft Company, by a scientist unassociated with any military endeavours. Yet as one of the largest defence electronics companies in the United States, deriving the overwhelming bulk of its nearly $500 million in annual sales from research, development and production for military agencies, Hughes was in an unusual position to speculate about, if not clearly foresee, the military potentialities in its then modest laser research. Before the company publicly announced its amazing results in the summer of 1960, it was already negotiating the first of what was subsequently to become many contracts with the US Air Force.

That the first laser was not operated under direct military auspices is purely accidental. For nearly a year before the Hughes announcement, American industry and military were buzzing with news of what was even then anticipated as an impending development of major importance, and probably of potentially great military value. Only a few months after Dr Charles H. Townes, later to be named a Nobel laureate for physics, and his brother-in-law, Dr Arthur Schawlow, published their now-famous paper on optical masers (lasers) in 1959 (see Chapter 1), several organizations were trying to make one operate with money supplied by the Department of Defence and the US Air Force. The far-ranging implications of these devices, in communications and radar especially, were clearly under-stood even then.

Death rays ?

There was even more, however. There was a pervading belief, then as now, but certainly more then than now, that the laser might constitute a step toward the ultimate in weapons, the long-sought elixir of weaponry, a destructive 'death ray' or radiation weapon. How seriously or how widely this idea was held in the days before the actual inception of the laser in 1960 is difficult to assess. Only an unanticipated declassification of the relevant military and industrial papers can answer these questions definitively. But the fact that early documents discussed this possibility, or the writers felt compelled to dispute it, attests to its prevalence. The normally candid Dr Townes, then a consultant to the Department of Defence, did little to dispel the notion, which had already circulated among the press, by his seemingly evasive answers to questioning on this subject by news reporters on at least one occasion that I witnessed.

The 'death ray' notion was an enticing one, and remains so to this day. The idea of a weapon whose destructive power could travel at the speed of light, rather than the comparatively snail-like ballistic pace, that could travel over great distances, and that could concentrate its power into secure, narrow beams was alluring — even though it might later prove illusory. Much of the belief in laser 'death rays' is now dismissed as naïve, based on what are viewed as misconceptions about the enormity of the actual problems and actual damage thresholds; these today are a closely-guarded secret. The talk then was of power density,[33] the high power that could be projected by the narrow, highly collimated laser beam over a small solid angle. Now, apparently, military scientists recognize that it is total energy on the target, not exceptionally high power density, which is necessary to destroy targets thermally.

The laser radiation weapon was conceived primarily as a quixotic answer to the growing recognition, at the turn of the decade, of the desperate need for a military defence against intercontinental ballistic missiles. The essential problem of missile defence, still essentially un-solved, is to find sufficient time to destroy the incoming warhead after it has penetrated the atmosphere, where it can more easily be detected, distinguished from accompanying decoys and tracked. Once the missile is properly identified and tracked, the position at which a defensive weapon can intercept it must be calculated and transferred to a hastily launched anti-missile. What makes the laser attractive is that, with its beam travelling at the speed of light, it can span relatively short distances in milliseconds, rather than minutes. This would virtually do away with the intercept computation since there would be little time-lapse between firing the laser 'death ray' and its impact on the target. Furthermore, since the intercept could occur virtually instantaneously, the ground discrimination radar could delay its job longer, permitting the atmosphere to burn up decoys which ordinarily confuse it at earlier points in their trajectories. The defence weapon would also be non-nuclear, lessening the hazards of radioactive fall-out.

A convincing quantitative argument against the validity of the anti-missile radiation weapon or 'death ray' has been presented by Professor Hans Thirring,[34] who, as Professor of Theoretical Physics at Vienna University, was one of the first scientists to predict, after Hiroshima, the possibility of an H-bomb. He estimates that 62,500 BTU or 13.45 kilowatt-hours of energy would be required to heat 100 lb of steel shielding, protecting a hypothetical warhead, to its melting point. To destroy the warhead when it has descended to 50 kilometres altitude, and to do this in a minute, requires 807 kilowatts for transferring the necessary destructive energy to the target. All of the energy generated by the laser will not strike the target, owing to some beam divergence. Thirring estimates that for a beam divergence of one minute of arc the beam's cross-sectional area at the required altitude would be 165 sq. metres, roughly 200 times the cross-section of his warhead. Thus, only half a per cent of the power carried by the beam would strike the target. Consequently, the laser would have to generate 200×807 kilowatts or 161.4 megawatts to do its job. This was eleven orders of magnitude greater than the milliwatt power level of continuous-wave lasers performing in 1963, he pointed out. The subsequent rise in laser output power levels to hundreds of watts shaves five orders of magnitude off the difference, but does little to invalidate his contention.

He also mentions the difficulty of aiming the narrow laser beam at the target — a task recognized long ago but only recently really appreciated by those looking at space communications with lasers. There are other arguments on both sides of the 'death ray' question. Some contend that the warhead need only be damaged or penetrated, thereby possibly lowering power requirements. Others argue that the chances of a fundamental limitation on the amount of energy that can be transmitted through a column of the atmosphere would preclude this application even if the power could be generated by the laser. In any case, the cost of such a weapon would be staggering.

Although the laser 'death ray', at least conceived as a destructive weapon, may be a myth, the quest for the laser 'death ray' certainly is not. Millions of dollars in research funds have been poured into investigations of such ideas in the USA[35]. The US Government invests over $100 million each year under its *Project Defender* in examining possible solutions — many of which it regards as being extremely remote — to the difficult problem of ballistic missile defence.

In view of this, one should not attach too much significance to the expenditure of millions of dollars annually on an idea that at best is questionable and at worst is a 'myth'. Sizeable amounts also have been spent on other ideas like ball lightning and microwave radiation weapons,[36] which might be equally nonsensical. But competent Defence Department officials would defend their encouragement of these programmes on the ground that they must explore all possible avenues in their search for a missile defence — including a few that the scientific community may dismiss as far-fetched. In any event, the knowledge accumulated in these activities, and particularly in laser research, may be useful in other respects.

Military interest in lasers, of course, extends well beyond missile defence. It finds quantitative expression in the funds made available to industrial and research organizations throughout the United States for research and development in lasers. During 1965, for example, the Defence Department spent $30.6 million on 176 separate laser projects.[37] These divide as follows:

Basic studies: 43 projects; $4.9 million
Device technology: 56 projects; $9.2 million
Materials research: 16 projects; $3 million
Applications: 48 projects; $12 million
Miscellaneous, including biological effects and instrumentation: 13 projects; $1.5 million.

Annual government expenditure has increased exponentially since 1959 when the Department of Defence's underwriting of original laser research barely topped $1 million. In only seven years the accumulated Defence Department spending for lasers approaches $100 million. Adding to these estimates at least one dollar spent by industry for each dollar of government research money received by it — a generally accepted rule of thumb — would indicate that almost $200 million may have been invested in laser research and development of at least passing interest to the US defence establishment in much less than a decade.

As the 1965 figures indicate, even by 1965 when lasers were approaching the threshold of applicability to military systems, only a fraction of the funds went for application research and development. In 1965 the figure was less than one-third, and this presumably is a new high point.

Range-finding by laser

Most of the immediate attention on the use of lasers in weapon systems in the USA, as in Western Europe and the Soviet Union, centres on tactical applications. The single category of applications which appears immediately practical is that of range-finding. This use relies on the simple determination of the round-trip transit time of laser pulses between the firing time and return, as in microwave radar, to measure range. But in each of the several possible ranging applications — ground-to-ground, air-to-ground, ground-to-space and air-to-air — the laser's unusual properties endow it with unrivalled performance.

Perhaps the first operational use of lasers will be as battlefield range-finders. Several portable laser range-finders have been built for use by foot soldiers or in tanks to determine precise range to enemy tanks, personnel carriers or fortifications. These devices have demonstrated an ability to measure range within several feet at distances of several or more miles. Commenting before US Senate-Defence Department budget hearings, the Army Assistant Deputy Chief of Staff for Logistics, Major General F. J. Chesarek, said that a proposed procurement of the XM23 laser range-finder would be the Army's first operational equipment based on laser technology. The pulsed ruby device would be carried, according to the general, by forward artillery observers as an aid in locating targets. This is a function now being performed by approximation and firing to correct range, a time-consuming calculation that by definition precludes the first-round hits that modern military forces are seeking.

Because the laser beams are non-divergent over battlefield distances their accuracy is virtually independent of range. The narrow laser beam permits the user to pinpoint his target without fear that his returns come from trees or harmless objects near the target.

By using compact lasers, simple power supplies and counter circuitry, all tightly packaged, some organizations in the USA and Europe have built range-finders weighing about 20 lb (see also Chapter 9). Several European countries, including West Germany, are evaluating tank and field army laser range-finders. The main battle tank for the 1970s, the MBT-70, a joint development of the armies of the Federal Republic of Germany and the USA, will have a laser range-finder in its fire control system. Soviet literature suggests that the Russians, too, are concentrating much of their military laser effort on tactical applications, including range-finding.[38]

While the battlefield range-finder appeared practical several years ago, assuming normal engineering progress toward making the device portable, temperature sensitivity posed a stumbling block, especially for cold climates. In cold weather, ruby range-finders tend to 'double-pulse' as a result of a build-up in gain in the ruby crystal. Double-pulsing in turn results in spurious range measurements. Heating the ruby to limit the gain can overcome this problem, but at the expense of clamping the device in a low-power mode. Other methods, such as using Q-switches for bunching energy into a single pulse, also are employed.

A slight variation on the battlefield range-finder application, now under intensive study in the United States, is to make the range-finder airborne by putting it in a helicopter, permitting the pilot or crew member to sight a target through a stabilized sight, obtain range to it by firing the laser which is slaved to the telescope's line of sight. This information can then be relayed via a data link to an artillery command, where computers can calculate an enemy's position. This is called an airborne target locator system, and is under development. Similarly, a small fixed-wing aircraft could be the laser platform.

Figure 36 Lightweight laser illuminator, developed by Westinghouse Electric, USA. It enables a ground observer to pinpoint a target. A remotely launched homing missile or semi-homing shell would then home on the laser spectral energy reflected from the target.

73

Laser illuminator

Another battlefield laser application which is absorbing American military attention is that of the man-portable laser illuminator (see Fig. 36). This device[39] is intended to solve another tough military problem. An observer on the ground encounters an enemy target and calls for aerial fire support or artillery. He describes his target or provides a rough co-ordinate indication. A supporting pilot in his high-speed aircraft frequently cannot precisely pick out the target, and risks striking his own comrades should he release his weapons in-opportunely. This becomes an even more complicated problem under

Figure 37 Tests in California on a neodymium-glass laser rangefinder, built by the Autonetics Division of North American Aviation. The white dome houses a multi-mode radar, and the laser-radar combination is one with great potential as an airborne system.

conditions of guerrilla warfare where verification of enemy location by visual sighting from the air is more unlikely. With the laser illuminator, the observer would call for a missile, then illuminate his target. Launched from a supporting aircraft the missile would have a terminal seeker head that could sense the laser energy reflected from the target and home on it.

There are several variations of the airborne and ground target ranging and illuminator concepts which give ground troops effective remote strike control. The supporting aircraft, in one configuration under evaluation in the USA, would carry a terrain-viewing television that could detect reflected laser energy and display it for the pilot on his screen, presumably superimposing it on a radar screen. The pilot then could direct his actions against the identified target.

The military prefers, wherever possible, to work at wavelengths which are not visible to the naked eye, to preserve operational security. This desire dictates a choice at this stage of development of the 1.06 micron wavelength of the neodymium-doped glass laser for which technology is relatively highly refined (as Chapter 3 has indicated). Figure 37 illustrates one application. But the ruby laser, whose output is visible, has other advantages including its operation at wavelengths for which there are detectors with superior efficiency.

The illuminator application is one for which secretiveness would be desirable. If a non-visible wavelength like that of the neodymium laser were used, a pilot would need vision-aided goggles to spot it. The illuminator, in any case, must generate sufficiently high average output power, and the reflected energy must have enough high persistence for the homing missile, a detector or the human eye to lock on to it. General Dynamics, one of the major manufacturers of naval and marine tactical missiles, announced that it had demonstrated the ability of a ground-launched supersonic missile to hit a 4 ft square target illuminated by a cooled gallium arsenide laser beam. Military research has, however, emphasized either ruby or neodymium-glass devices for battlefield use because they do not require refrigeration.

The US Army also regards the use of a laser illuminator in a semi-active homing approach as a method of improving the accuracy of helicopter fire power. In this case the helicopter-launched weapon would derive its guidance information from a laser beam illuminating the target from the helicopter. Still another laser guidance concept, which is looked upon as slightly beyond the reach of current technology, would involve a completely self-contained laser guidance system within an air-launched missile. Roughly, this is comparable to operational types of radar-guided air-to-ground or air-to-air missiles, in which a target detected and tracked by the aircraft radar fire control is handed over to the missile, whose laser head is slaved to the fire control radar. Once the laser is locked on to target, the missile would be released, to guide itself to its target.

Airborne range-finding

Perhaps one of the most promising and unexpected weapons applications for lasers, and the one likely to find, along with the battlefield range-finder, the most extensive use in the next several years, will be the air-to-ground range-finder. There are a number of reasons for the sudden recognition and surge of interest in this application. The importance of ranging information for tactical aircraft has been overlooked in the haste to develop nuclear weapons and nuclear delivery tactics. Gross delivery accuracy is acceptable for nuclear weapons because of their great destructive power. But conventional bombs and rockets must be placed on assigned targets accurately if they are to be effective.

With the installation of forward-looking, multi-mode radar in modern military aircraft, few people foresaw any possible use for the laser in aircraft fire control systems. Then, in recent years, military planners became aware that the best way for penetrating aircraft to elude detection by air defence radars was to fly extremely low over the terrain. In this way, the presence of the aircraft would be hidden in the ground 'clutter' (noise) on radar screens. The so-called low-altitude penetration tactics created a comparable problem in reverse for the attacker. Attack radars operated at low angles with respect to the ground, or at low grazing or low approach angles, suffer the same degradation that a ground-based radar experiences when it scans too close to its horizon in search of low-flying aircraft. Its returns are swamped by ground clutter.

The laser beam, however, is extremely narrow compared with microwave radar beams, and it can range successfully at far smaller grazing angles, 5 degrees or less compared with 15 degrees, before it is bothered by spurious responses. It is true that in foul weather laser light is absorbed or scattered by moisture, severely restricting its usefulness. But in tactical applications a pilot usually must be able to see his target, and if the weather is bad enough to preclude use of the laser it presumably also would prevent him from observing his target. Furthermore, cloud cover is more likely to clear at low altitudes.

During the latter part of 1965, the US Air Force successfully tested an airborne laser range-finder in a modern, radar-equipped high-performance fighter of the type used by the American Air Force and Navy, and destined for delivery to the Royal Air Force and Navy. Part of what is called a visual attack fire control system,[40] the laser range-finder, housed in a small bubble beneath the aircraft's radome (Fig. 38), has significantly improved the accuracy of bomb and rocket delivery.

The tested system consists of the ruby laser ranging device, an analogue weapons delivery computer and an optical sight (Fig. 39). The pilot flies his aircraft with steering instructions from the sight.

Figure 38   Laser head, mounted in a bubble beneath the forward radome of a Phantom fighter, for flight evaluation of the laser fire control system shown in Figure 39.

Since the laser line-of-sight is slaved to the optical sight's line-of-sight, the laser can range off targets and feed this information to the computer. Similarly, attitude and velocity data obtained from the aircraft's inertial navigation system are fed to the computer, which calculates the time to release weapons and pull out. Its small size allows the laser to be installed as a sensor to supplement forward-looking radar in high-performance aircraft, as it was in this test system, or as a visual attack system in lighter aircraft. Essentially, it is the laser's simplicity, its inherent reliability and its ease of maintenance — compared with radar — which makes it so attractive in tactical applications.

Many of the newer American attack aircraft will probably be fitted with a laser for ranging, for low light level television illumination, or for reconnaissance. For those aircraft which cannot support expensive and bulky radar, the laser ranging device may fulfil an important need. Aircraft without inertial navigation platforms might still use a full visual attack system deriving navigation information

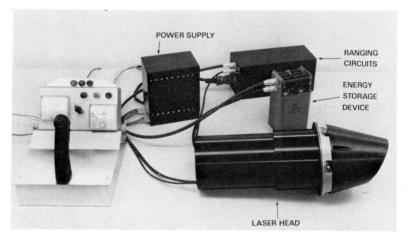

Figure 39 Laser ground-to-air rangefinder includes ruby laser transmitter, receiver, power supply, ranging circuitry and energy storage system. This rangefinder, made by Hughes Aircraft, has undergone successful flight tests for the US Air Force.

from air data sources. Experiences in Vietnam suggest that light, piston-engined aircraft, which do not have the power or space for complicated modern electronic systems, may have important military functions in which the laser range-finder may play a part.

The laser range-finder, working in conjunction with an optical sight, could eliminate range errors in bombing missions by giving the pilot a precise idea of his distance from the target. Range to the target could be set into the system before the mission and once the aircraft reaches its destination the pilot might release his weapons. His sight would be servo-ed to the laser and a range symbol corresponding to the time-to-release could indicate weapon release.

For air-to-ground weapons delivery, a pilot must have knowledge of attitude, airspeed, distance from the target and power setting to place the aircraft at predetermined bomb release velocity and attitude for accurate hits. Wind velocity at release altitude also is needed. Ordinarily the pilot estimates these factors and positions his aircraft accordingly. The visual attack system handles the entire problem, permitting him to devote himself to flying his optical sight.[41]

Military requirements seem aimed at airborne range-finders having repetition rates of three to ten pulses per second for reasonable periods, and the ability to achieve these rates without cooling. The neodymium-doped glass laser has lower thresholds and lower power at short ranges, which may give it the edge over ruby under these conditions; but at the longer ranges ruby's better thermal properties and higher efficiency, and the availability of more efficient detectors, may give it the advantage.

An air-to-air range-finder laser has been successfully flight tested by the US Navy at its Ordnance Test Station in China Lake, California. A possible potential use for the laser range-finder in an air-to-air mode is as an aid in determining when a target is within range of an attacking aircraft's weapons. Again the compact nature and lightness of the laser enable it to be installed for this purpose. Similarly, the US Army's Electronics Command contracted with Honeywell Incorporated in late 1965 to develop a laser obstacle avoidance device that would detect wires or other obstructions to low-flying spotter aircraft. The high resolution of the laser makes it suitable for this task.

Laser surveillance

The laser also offers a promising answer to another tough military need — night-time reconnaissance. The requirements for nocturnal aerial surveillance was nowhere more apparent than in the Cuban crisis or the conflict in Vietnam. The ability of an enemy to move troops and supplies unhindered in the open at night, or to set up transportable anti-aircraft missile sites, emphasizes this need. Traditionally, night-time photographic reconnaissance has been accomplished with the aid of magnetic flares or powerful strobe lights, which not only alert an enemy but assist him in combatting his antagonist by clearly indicating his presence in the sky.

A laser line-scanning camera system is an answer to this difficulty. It can obtain pictures at night which are comparable to, or better than, the quality of those obtained under favourable daylight conditions by an aerial photographic reconnaissance system. Photographs taken with one early, relatively primitive system afford qualitative evidence of this. The system, tested by the US Air Force early in 1965, employed a commercially-available, continuous-wave helium-neon laser having only 20 milliwatts output.[42] The pictures obtained from aircraft flying at relatively low altitudes, generally less than 3,000 ft, reveal a clarity which is startling for a system at such an early stage of development. Motor cars, houses, footpaths and shrubbery are clearly visible in one picture of a typical American residential community. A photograph of an airport runway reveals a myraid of tiny cracks, normally not visible to the human eye; these stand out owing to light absorption.

For military missions this approach offers the advantage of quasi-secretive operation not previously available for a photographic

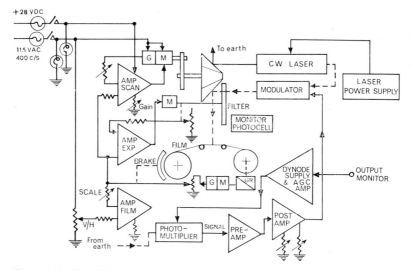

Figure 40 Simplified block diagram of a laser line scanning camera system developed by Perkin-Elmer for night reconnaissance. The quality of photographs taken in this way is quite remarkable.

system at night. Even when a visible laser line is employed, as with a helium-neon gas laser, the beam is so narrow and non-divergent that there is little likelihood a ground observer would see it unless he happened to gaze directly at it. Sideways-looking radar can perform night-time reconnaissance, and has been put to use in combat in Vietnam, but the laser will provide pictures of superior resolution — a function of the shorter wavelength of the radiation used. But the laser system would, of course, be inhibited in the presence of cloud cover, a burden not shared by sideways-looking radar.

The principle on which the system works is relatively simple. As indicated in Fig. 40, the laser beam is split in two, with one beam passing through a Pockels cell modulator, striking a rotating, six-sided prism scanner that reflects it on to film, which records it. The camera's function is that of a recording device only, supplying film with its large bandwidth and resolution storage capability.

A second portion of the beam, which directly strikes the scanner, is reflected down to the terrain below. The prism scans the beam through some preselected angle, perhaps 30 or 40 degrees in the lateral direction, or at right-angles to the direction of flight of the aircraft. The movement of the aircraft provides the scan in the forward direction.

Light energy reflected from the terrain is then picked up by a Schmidt lens, which images the light on to a photomultiplier detector. The video output from the latter, which corresponds to the reflectivity of the scanned terrain, drives the modulator, impressing a time-varying signal on the basic laser carrier. The system scans the laser line at a rate of several hundred lines a second with aircraft travelling at 100 to 300 knots. Resolution in this early system was between $\frac{1}{2}$ and 2 milliradians.

Several organizations are pursuing this development and, while the specific directions of their efforts are unknown, it is reasonable to assume they are resorting to the use of higher power, continuous-wave lasers to improve resolution and/or to permit operation at higher altitudes. More efficient non-mechanical scanning techniques certainly are available and can be applied advantageously.

A more powerful continuous-wave laser, such as an ionized argon device (Chapter 3), capable of generating tens of watts rather than the milliwatts of the helium-neon laser, offers one clue to the potentialities of the reconnaissance application. A laser of this type offers a 50-decibel improvement in performance, estimated on the basis of four orders of magnitude increase in output power and a ten-fold improvement in photo-cathode efficiency at the 4880-angstrom wavelength of argon devices. Either operation from higher altitudes or substantial gains in resolution, or some suitable combination of the two, could be secured in this way.

Those properties of the laser of chief concern in its application to tactical reconnaissance are the narrowness of its beam, which defines the resolution of the scanning system, and the beam's radiance, or brightness, which determines how much energy is projected into the far field.

Multi-mode laser systems

Multi-mode laser devices probably will come into vogue once the laser has established itself firmly as a useful part of airborne weapon systems, as now seems likely. One such combination, as developed by Westinghouse Electric, is a ruby laser air-to-ground ranging system and target illuminator for low light level television. Aligned with, and slaved to, a stabilized optical sight, the laser could provide sufficient illumination for low light level television, a relatively new technique finding favour among the military services, the outputs of which could be displayed for target selection by the pilot or crew. Once the target is selected, the laser might be switched into another mode for measuring range to the target. In the system being developed, the device would have a low pulse rate — about four pulses a minute. In one mode it could measure the range of targets selected by the pilot from his optical sight. In a second mode it could offer target illumination for television while operating at higher data rates in a beam-spoiled condition.

During 1966, the US Army evaluated in operations over Vietnam and at test centres in North America a number of applications for lasers in helicopters. The encouraging performance of helicopters as weapons platforms is giving rise to many promising laser uses besides the semi-active missile guidance aid and forward artillery observer functions cited earlier. A range-finder comparable to that described for fixed-wing aircraft seems likely to go into production, now that US Army helicopters are to be equipped with more sophisticated weapons. For example, a decision to develop a helicopter version of the US Army's TOW (tube-launched, optically sighted, wire-guided) anti-tank missile illustrates this point. Because the weapon's range is a function of the wire which unravels behind the missile as it streaks toward its target and through which it receives terminal guidance commands from its operator, the laser can help in giving accurate indications when targets come within maximum range. Similarly, the laser can be integrated into fire-control systems to boost accuracy of grenade launchers and cannon now expected to find increasingly common use in helicopters. The US Army's advanced aerial fire support system (AAFSS), the first helicopter to be designed from its inception as a weapons-carrying platform, will carry three different types of tactical weapons for which a laser range-finder will be a key fire-control element in computing superelevation angles.

A combination range-finder and low light level television illuminator underwent trials in Vietnam in 1966. The US Army hopes to use low light level television as a sensor for enabling helicopters to fly low, along the 'nap-of-the-earth', at night as well as during the day to avoid detection and hostile ground fire. While low light level television appears promising the pilot does not get sufficient depth perception confidently to judge his height above the terrain. By integrating the laser range-finder with the television camera, the US Army expects to give its pilots that needed third dimension in the form of continuous altitude readings. What remains to be seen, however, is whether the same laser can provide, nearly simultaneously, both illumination and ranging information since these require what appear to be contradictory characteristics — that is, a diffuse beam for illumination and a sharp beam with well-defined leading edges of laser pulses.

Satellite surveillance

A satellite surveillance capability has been the goal of about four years of development, progressing at an apparently disappointing pace. A laser tracking station has been built at Cloudcroft, New Mexico, high above the arid southwestern desert, where dry weather favours good laser operating conditions. A similar facility is planned for Mount Haleakala on the island of Maui in Hawaii. One of the problems with the former station at least is that advances in laser technology have outdated the laser transmitter before it has gone into operation. The basic concept appears to be a valid one — using the narrow, high-power laser beam to track non-co-operative space objects. Relatively high energy ruby lasers are expected to enable these installations to track and possibly to illuminate satellites hundreds of miles away at night. Projecting light on to the front of a satellite, and photographing it through an optical telescope, might yield details of alien satellites not possible by other means.

The armed services have many plans for lasers, some beyond the reach of present technology but still well within the realm of possibility. Secure, short-range line-of-sight battlefield communications using gallium arsenide lasers has been under intensive study with security afforded by the narrow beam being the attraction. High-power missile defence radars, possibly capable of handling the decoy discrimination job by virtue of the high inherent angular resolution provided by laser radar (lidar), may be one of the remote, but conceivable future applications. Electronically scanned laser displays, pulsed and continuous-wave laser altimeters, laser data processing and laser alignment of inertial navigation platforms are a few of the many laser applications in varying stages of development by the military.

Because of the excitement surrounding laser developments, the device has found applications which some scientists regard as questionable. They work; but can the job be done just as easily and perhaps more economically by other ways? Or does the application really merit the introduction of a laser? The airborne laser 'scoring' system, in which detectors in one aircraft provide an indication of whether a chase aircraft, using a laser aligned with its weapons, has scored a 'hit', much as the photocell in an amusement park rifle range target senses a hit by a toy gun, may be a case in point.

Although virtually nothing is publicly mentioned about it, the game of counter-measures and counter-countermeasures is being enacted with lasers as it is on other electro-magnetic levels. The Russians have reported a method of transforming pulsed outputs from high power injection lasers into d.c. voltages, a technique which is applicable to a system that 'would electronically pinpoint the physical presence of either an infrared laser ranging or communications beam. Not only would this device warn of tactical penetration by enemy laser systems and thus cause counter-measure action, but in conjunction with the laser transmitter, it could give the source location of that detected beam'.

Similarly, the US Department of Commerce's *Business Daily*, which is required by law to publish contract awards by government agencies, has reported development efforts seeking counter-measures against such weapons as infrared laser guided missiles. It is reasonable to infer from this that counter-measures against each military application of the laser are at least under study.

No less is it reasonable to suspect that the intense heat generated by laser beams, while of dubious effectiveness against ballistic missiles, may be fatal to sensitive infrared detectors. A laser properly aimed at an infrared homing missile conceivably could damage sensitive heat-seeking elements, thereby rendering them harmless. Other direct non-lethal laser weapons may be imagined.

Several years of research for the US Air Force's Avionics Laboratory has resulted in a so-called 'instantaneous' optical shutter for protecting optical devices like infrared sensors from damage by bursts of high-intensity optical radiation, such as that generated by lasers. The normally transparent shutter goes opaque when struck by ruby laser pulses, for example, then recovers its transparent qualities. It can withstand successive bursts of light and has the unusually good property of reaching complete opacity more quickly as the pulse energy increases.

The human eye itself is, of course, a sensitive light detector which may be the vulnerable target of anti-personnel laser radiation weapons comparable to what might be directed against infrared detectors or photographic and television cameras. Anti-personnel weapons are within the realm of laser technology. One can conjecture about those distasteful military situations in which a short-range laser radiation weapon projecting sufficient energy to blind an opponent might be a desirable weapon. Close combat, with friendly troops wearing protective goggles, is one possibility. Capturing a tank without destroying or damaging it, or eliminating its 'eyes', is another.

It is, perhaps, too early in the evolution of laser technology to predict how important a role lasers will play in weapons. From the start the military has regarded the laser as a potentially important military device. Many technical people closely associated with weapon systems development are already convinced that the discovery of the laser will at least rank in military significance with the development of infrared and radar technology.

7

THE LASER AS A SOURCE OF HEAT

DR KENNETH FIRTH

Associated Electrical Industries Ltd, Rugby

When light is absorbed, the energy can reappear as heat. This has long been familiar in the 'burning glass' which uses the focused rays of the Sun to ignite combustible materials. More recently, high-temperature solar furnaces and arc image furnaces have been developed, enabling the most refractory materials to be melted. However, the second law of thermodynamics indicates that the temperature of the material being heated cannot exceed the (effective) temperature of the emitting source. The effective temperature of the Sun's radiation is about 6000°K, and that of the most intense arcs is not much greater than 10,000°K.

The equivalent temperature of high-power, 'Q-switched' laser beams has been estimated by Townes[43] to be as high as 10^{23}°K (Q-switching is a technique for building up very powerful laser pulses, discussed in Chapter 9, p. 124). This astronomical figure arises because the laser's output is confined to a very small angle and a very small range of wavelengths, and the 'equivalent black body' emits uniformly into a hemisphere over a wide wavelength range.

For practical purposes, power per unit area is a more useful yardstick than equivalent temperature. For instance, it is not very difficult to achieve a power density of 10^{12} watts per sq. cm by focusing the output of a Q-switched laser; this is to be compared with 50 kilowatts per sq. cm at the surface of a black body at 10,000°K. To indicate what is possible by other means, a billion watts per sq. cm is quite difficult to achieve using a focused electron beam, although relatively easy to obtain using a laser. The ease of obtaining high peak power densities in this way is the basis of the interest in the laser as a source of heat. At the same time, the low average powers obtainable until quite recently were the reason for the short duration of the interest in many cases.

Theoretical aspects

In discussing the heating effects produced by laser beams, it is instructive to consider the results of a simplified theory. First, let us consider heating by continuous laser beams. If a uniform circular beam, of radius a and power W, falls perpendicularly upon the surface of a material of thermal conductivity K, and the beam is totally absorbed in a distance small compared with a, then the equilibrium temperature rise T at the centre of the circular area is given by

$$T = \frac{W}{\pi K a}.$$

This result is exact only so long as the thickness of the material is large compared with a. If this is the case, the surfaces of constant temperature at a distance from the centre of the beam large compared to a are hemispheres, and the temperature at a distance R from the origin is $\frac{W}{2\pi KR}$. Thus, we see that the heating effect of a continuous beam is highly localized. If the material is thin compared to the radius of the incident beam, then the temperature drop across the material is often negligible and the surfaces of constant temperature are approximately cylindrical. No simple expression can be given for the surface temperatures in this case. The detailed equations can be found in an article by Fairbanks and Adams.[44]

In the case of a pulsed laser beam, we must consider transient conditions. Near the surface the flow of heat is characterized by a plane wave; that is, heat conduction in directions perpendicular to the beam can be neglected. So the surface temperature, T, during this phase (which holds for times, t, up to the order of $\frac{a^2}{\kappa}$) depends only on the power per unit area, and not upon the size of the beam. (NB $\kappa = \frac{K}{\rho c}$ is the thermal diffusivity of the material, where K is the thermal conductivity, ρ the density and c the specific heat.) It is given by:

$$T = \frac{2W}{\pi a^2} \left(\frac{t}{\pi \rho c K} \right)^{\frac{1}{2}}$$

If the duration of the pulse is greater than about $5\frac{a^2}{\kappa}$, then the value of T approaches the equilibrium value for a continuous beam. For intermediate pulse durations, the expressions are complicated.

Practical considerations

The results given above naturally assume that no phase changes occur; that is, that the substance heated does not melt or vaporize, and that the thermal 'constants' are independent of the surface temperature. In many cases of interest phase changes do occur and the thermal constants do vary appreciably with surface temperature. But the equations are nonetheless of value in predicting qualitatively what is likely to happen under given conditions.

A further restriction of the validity of the equations given, as I have already mentioned, is that absorption of light must be complete in a distance small compared to a. Since in metals light absorption is virtually complete in distances that are small compared to the wavelength of light, and the minimum value of a theoretically attainable is of the order of one wavelength, this condition is always fulfilled. However, in this case we should expect reflection to have a very significant effect on the fraction of the incident light which is actually absorbed. In practice, it does not appear to be as significant as one

Figure 41 Transparent specimen reveals internal fractures caused by a powerful laser pulse fired into one end of the Lucite rod. (*Courtesy, Martin Company, USA.*)

would expect from room-temperature values of reflectivity — at any rate when vaporization takes place.

In the case of lightly absorbing materials, the equations given are not even approximately correct, but it is possible nevertheless to make a simple estimate of the rate of rise of temperature. Suppose, for instance, that only 1 per cent of the beam is absorbed in a distance of 1 cm, and that the initial power density is 10^{12} watts per sq. cm. Then (neglecting conduction losses) the rate of heating in a material of heat capacity 1 joule per cubic cm is 10 billion °C per second; that is, 1000°C in a tenth of a microsecond.

Thus, even 'transparent' materials can be heated significantly (Fig. 41). This has been shown experimentally by the fact that holes can be drilled by a laser beam in alumina, and even in diamonds. However, it should be pointed out that, although in the case of alumina melting occurs around the periphery of the hole produced, it is not necessary to heat diamond to very high temperatures in order to drill it. This is because diamond is transformed into graphite. Steigerwald[45] has shown that, in the presence of oxygen, holes can be drilled in diamond using an electron beam which heats the surface to only about 450°C.

In considering the possibility of using the laser as a heat source of very high power density, the minimum value of the beam radius, a, is of great interest. The minimum value theoretically attainable, which is determined by diffraction at the aperture of the lens used to focus the beam, is given by $a_{min} = \dfrac{0.61\lambda}{(\text{N.A.})}$, where N.A. is the numerical aperture of the lens used to focus the beam. Thus, the lower limit is $\sim \dfrac{\lambda}{2}$, using an immersion objective.

In practice, it is necessary for high-power applications to use air spaced objectives with considerably smaller numerical aperture. The value of a_{min} given above is not usually attainable with existing lasers since the beam divergence is not generally 'diffraction limited'. If the beam divergence is θ, then the minimum spot diameter is $f\theta$. Thus for $\theta = 1$ milliradian and $f = 1$ cm, $2a = 10^{-3}$ cm. For solid state lasers, in which the mirrors are deposited on the laser rod, θ can be as large as 10 milliradians, but 1 milliradian is not difficult to achieve in an external mirror system.

Choice of laser

The other important factor not so far considered is the power which can be attained in the laser beam. Table 6 shows maximum powers so far attained with lasers of various types, when operating continuously or pulsed.

Table 6. Maximum powers from lasers

Type	Max. CW Power	Max. Pulsed Power	Typical Pulse Lengths
Gas	~ 500 watts	up to 2×10^5 watts	10^{-6}—10^{-8} sec
Solid-state	~ 40 watts	10^5 watts (non Q-switched)	10^{-3} sec
		10^9 watts (Q-switched)	10^{-8} sec
Semiconductor	~ 10 watts	~ 100 watts	10^{-6} sec

The suitability of pulsed lasers for heating applications depends upon their mean power as well as peak power and pulse duration. At present the highest mean power outputs are obtained from doped crystal lasers and these almost exclusively have been used for heating applications.

Even so, up to the time of writing, mean powers obtainable are less than 100 watts. The limitation on mean power output at present arises from the effects of heat generated in the laser rod. These effects include line broadening, reduction in fluorescence quantum efficiency, changes in optical path length, and thermal stresses (which can cause fracture); the last two being due to non-uniform expansion of the laser crystal. The heat arises from the nature of the excitation process and cannot be entirely eliminated since light is always absorbed at one wavelength and emitted at a longer one (see Chapter 3). Even if thermal effects in the material can be overcome, the thermal effects in the flash tubes used for excitation will still impose a limitation; although an increase in overall efficiency from present values, typically less than 1 per cent, would alleviate this restriction.

The position with pulsed gas lasers, where mean power outputs are at present even lower, is somewhat similar to that for flash tubes. Increases in the mean output power of the pulsed argon laser, for example, depend on the development of improved tube wall materials and electrodes. However, the recent report of the attainment of peak powers up to 200 kW[46] (albeit in pulses lasting only 20 nanoseconds), in a configuration which reduces heat dissipation problems at the electrodes, make it unwise to dismiss the pulsed gas laser as a possible useful source in high mean power heating applications. It seems not improbable, too, that high peak powers can also be combined with high efficiencies; up to 15 per cent has been reported for the continuous wave nitrogen-carbon dioxide laser. Unlike other gas lasers this one can be Q-switched and in principle similar efficiencies should be attainable in this mode of operation at high pulse repetition frequencies.

On the other hand, it appears that the semiconductor laser (Chapter 4), although capable of very high efficiencies at low temperatures, is unlikely to achieve pulsed powers in excess of a kilowatt or so unless the material itself is greatly improved. This low peak power is due to the rapid rise in threshold and decrease in efficiency which occurs when the temperature of the junction rises during the pulse, through resistance heating at the contacts. Because of this limitation to low peak powers and low temperature environment, it seems unlikely that the pulsed semiconductor laser will find much use for heating applications.

The recent development of high-power continuously operating carbon dioxide lasers with outputs up to several hundred watts means that the laser may find considerable use in many heating applications not previously feasible.

'Low-temperature' applications

The expression 'low-temperature' I use to imply that the temperatures required are below the melting point (or sublimation point) of the material being heated; in other words, no gross change of phase is involved. One possible scientific application in this category is the use of the laser in the determination of thermal diffusivities by the 'flash' method. The laser could be used to apply a heat pulse to one side of a block of material and the resulting temperature change on the other side of the block measured as a function of time. Xenon flash tubes have previously been used in this method, but the laser in principle offers the possibility of working with smaller samples.

Turning to possible engineering applications, the laser could, in principle, be applied to the localized heat-treatment of metals and alloys — although no instance of its being attempted has come to my notice.

A similar application, which has frequently been suggested in the literature, is the possibility of using a laser beam to cause localized diffusion of impurities in the production of semiconductor devices. However, this would require a continuously operating laser and with the powers at present available, it would seem not to be feasible to process more than a few devices at a time, compared to the thousands which can be processed concurrently by conventional methods. In any case, the large temperature gradients, which are characteristic of localized heating, are undesirable in conventional devices. Thus, such a method would be justified only if it enabled one to manufacture a device of novel characteristics, not produced readily by other means.

Another low-temperature application which has been suggested concerns the use of pulsed laser heating to give enhanced thermionic emission for short periods, to enable high peak power short pulses to be obtained from the cathodes of microwave transmitting valves. The pulsed heating would enable one to obtain high peak emission currents without a sustained high cathode temperature (and consequent short cathode life). A number of laboratory studies of this effect have been published and the expected effect has been observed.

Welding applications

The possibility of using the laser for welding has attracted considerable interest from the outset, and it has been shown experimentally that pulsed lasers can be used for welding in a limited range of material sizes. Continuously operating lasers with power outputs adequate for welding application are only just becoming available.

The factors to be considered in assessing the requirements for a pulsed laser welder are:

1. The power per unit area in the laser beam should not be so great as to cause appreciable vaporization of the metal.
2. Because of the limited mean power available, the peak power should be as great as possible to reduce heat conduction losses and thereby utilize the heat efficiently.
3. The pulse must last long enough to enable complete penetration of the melted zone to be achieved.

These conditions are conflicting and a compromise has to be found. It has been suggested by Kaplan,[47] on the basis of theoretical considerations, that the optimum pulse length is of the order of $\dfrac{L^2}{2\kappa}$ where L is the thickness of the material and κ is its thermal diffusivity. Values of this parameter for a number of different materials and thicknesses are given in Table 7.

Table 7. Thermal time constant of typical metals [47]

Metal	Thickness		
	0.005 in	0.025 in	0.125 in
Aluminium	0.12 millisec	3.0 millisec	74 millisec
Copper	0.08	2.1	52
Iron	0.57	14.0	360
Stainless steel	1.40	35.0	890
Tantalum	0.34	8.7	220
Titanium	1.50	38.0	940
Tungsten	0.13	3.2	80

We see from Table 7 that for materials of poor thermal conductivity, such as stainless steel, pulse lengths greater than 10 milliseconds are required, even for material only 0.025 in thick. These qualitative results of Kaplan are supported by the more detailed

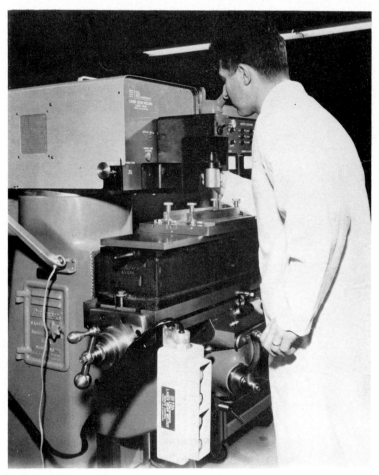

Figure 42 Laser beam welder developed by TRG Inc., USA, for welding experiments on refractory metals.

theory of Fairbanks and Adams.[44] Since pulse lengths greater than a few milliseconds are technically difficult to achieve, and working with long pulses tends to reduce the already low efficiency of laser systems, laser welding would appear to be attractive only for thin materials of fairly high thermal conductivity. Nevertheless TRG Inc. has recently been awarded a contract by the US Air Force to develop their existing laser welder (Fig. 42), said to be capable of welding material up to 0.0625 in thick, to enable materials up to 0.125 in thick to be welded, using pulse lengths in the 20 to 40 millisecond range.

The most comprehensive experimental report on laser welding is probably that given by Anderson and Jackson of the Linde Division of Union Carbide,[48] who report that they have produced good welds in a variety of materials; moreover, that their results are in good agreement with the theory of Fairbanks and Adams. They used a ruby laser with an output of up to 20 joules and pulse lengths of 1 to 4 milliseconds. Welds between similar and dissimilar metal wires have been made and tested for strength and electrical resistance.

Table 8 shows their results for butt, lap, tee and crossed wire-to-wire welds. About 10 joules are required to produce a weld as strong as the wire itself, for 0.015 in diameter wire. Generally, they find that the weld strength is high and the electrical resistance is low. They also report successful sheet-to-sheet pulsed seam welding, for an energy requirement about 1.5 times that for welding wires.

They expressed the opinion, which I share, that laser welding will find its largest single application in the electronics industry, probably in making connections to thin films, interconnections between integrated circuits, encapsulation, and so on. They stress the advantages of laser welding in minimizing thermal damage to other parts, and in not requiring direct contact with the workpiece. Electron-beam welding, which also has some of these advantages, requires that the components should be placed in a vacuum; thus laser welding has a distinct advantage. It appears that these views are also shared by the Westinghouse Electric Corporation's Aerospace Division, Baltimore, who are reported to have a laser welder on a routine production line for spot welding leads to conductors on printed circuit wiring boards.[49]

However, it remains to be seen how well the laser welder can compete economically with more prosaic processes such as thermocompression bonding, or even the use of microsoldering techniques using hot gases, for making most kinds of electrical connection.

Applications involving vaporization

The effects of a focused laser beam in vaporizing materials are among the most spectacular produced by lasers — although not perhaps so spectacular as the script writers of the film *Goldfinger* would have us believe. These effects vary considerably with the power density in the focused laser beam.

In the case of ordinary (non Q-switched) pulsed laser beams, Ready[50] has shown that the amounts of metal vaporized by a focused laser beam are consistent with a theory in which it is assumed that the energy in the laser pulse either causes evaporation of material from the surface or is lost by conduction into the bulk. The theory

Figure 43   Laser machining rig developed in the laboratories of Western Electric, USA, for drilling and milling operations.

also shows that in most cases of interest the conduction loss is small. The small differences observed between the theoretical esti-mate of the amount of material removed and the values found ex-perimentally indicate, as I have already mentioned, that reflection from the metal surface is not an important source of loss. Ready also concludes there is little absorption of the incoming radiation in the plume of vaporized material; that is, the time scale of the pulse is such that the vaporized material has time to leave the surface and move away without building up a highly absorbing ionized vapour layer.

This means that relatively deep holes can be produced; and indeed, holes have been drilled in half-inch steel plate using the focused beam from a ruby laser with an output of several hundred joules. While it is thus clear that the laser can be used for small-scale drilling and small machining jobs, as with laser welding, it is by no means clear that it will be economic to use the laser except in very specialized situations.

Evaporation is in any case an inefficient method of machining compared to conventional methods. It requires on average about 100,000 joules to evaporate a cubic centimetre of metal and, in cases where difficulty of using conventional machining methods make such methods economic, the laser must compete with electron-beam machining. This is a basically similar method which has the advantage that much higher mean powers are attainable and that manipulation of the beam is easily accomplished. However, it has the disadvantage of requiring that the workpiece must be placed under high vacuum, that considerable quantities of X-rays are generated and shielding must therefore be provided, and that it is very expensive to produce electron beams with the requisite power densities.

Thus it appears possible that the laser will find a useful place in the 'micro-machining' of difficult materials when low mean powers are adequate; for example, the manufacture of spinerettes used in fibre production, and in the production of miniature ferrite cores for use in computer stores. Fig. 43 shows the machining of metal by a laser beam. Lasers have already found production uses in trimming thin-film resistors and in the balancing of chronometer balance wheels without taking them apart, by using the laser to remove small amounts of material. Another specialized application, developed at the Atomic Energy Research Establishment, is illustrated in Fig. 44. More recently, the Western Electric Corporation has reported the production use of a pulsed ruby laser for drilling and trimming diamond dies used in wire drawing.

A further use of the normal pulse laser as a source of vapour has been reported by Honig and Woolston. They used it as an adjunct to a mass spectrometer ion source, with an auxiliary discharge through the vapour to produce ionization in the vaporized material.[51]

It has been found that the amount of material evaporated by focusing a Q-switched laser pulse on to the surface of a material is relatively small, compared with a normal laser pulse with the same energy. This can be explained by a hypothesis due to Ready.[50] It is postulated that the surface temperature of the material initially rises very rapidly to the vaporization temperature, emission of vapour begins and the material recoiling against the surface produces such a high recoil pressure that the boiling point of the underlying material is raised considerably. The emission of high-temperature material then proceeds very rapidly.

Archbold and his colleagues have shown[52] that surface temperatures in the region of 5000°K are attained, which is in agreement with this

Figure 44   A 50-joule ruby laser is used to puncture a radioactive nuclear fuel can, to release the fission gases for analysis. The fuel can is inside a glass vacuum vessel. The technique was developed at Atomic Energy Research Establishment, Harwell.

hypothesis. The vaporized material emitted at this stage, which is initially at the surface temperature, is then rapidly heated by the absorption of light during the remainder of the pulse. Archbold observed spectral lines characteristic of multiply ionized atoms, and deduced from these observations that the temperature of the vapour reaches at least 20,000°K.

Light absorption in the thermally ionized vapour is thought to be caused chiefly by the 'inverse Bremstrahlung' process involving the interaction of two free electrons and a photon. This process has a high probability because of the high electron density in the hot plasma. Ehler[53] has observed the emission of ions with energies of up to several hundred electron volts from plasmas produced by focusing a Q-switched laser on to metal surfaces in a vacuum. These results are somewhat difficult to account for on the basis of the simple picture described above.

A number of theoretical papers have appeared considering the use of focused laser beams for producing extremely hot plasmas in deuterium or hydrogen with the object of determining whether or not it would be feasible in principle to achieve a controlled thermonuclear reaction by this method. Tozer and his co-workers[54] concluded that, using magnetic containment of the plasma, temperatures of the order of a million °K should be attainable using present-day limits of field strength and photon flux — albeit in a very small volume, about a millionth of a cu. cm, near the focus of a focused laser beam. He further calculates that, to achieve a fusion reaction with net power output, laser energies greater than 10,000 joules for a single passage of radiation through the plasma, and magnetic field strengths greater than 100 million gauss, are required if the plasma is formed from a hydrogen pellet *in vacuo*. These conditions would hardly appear to be feasible in the near future,* altough Q-switched laser beams are being used to generate high temperature plasmas in a number of laboratories up to eighth order spectra have been observed by this means.

An early application of the plasma produced by Q-switched laser beams has been described by Brecht and others. They found that the light emitted by the plasma could be used for analysis of the vaporized material by emission spectroscopy, although in general an auxiliary spark-discharge was passed through the vapour. Since the struck area is very small, this method is complementary to X-ray microprobe analysis, especially for light elements. It has found a good deal of use in the USA, particularly for the analysis of biological samples.

---

*Editor's note: Westinghouse Research Laboratories, USA, have reported (Summer 1966) the generation of a plasma by vaporizing an aluminium pellet with a 100-megwatt pulse from a ruby laser. A magnetic 'bottle' sustained the plasma for 50 microseconds.

Table 8. Properties of wire-to-wire laser welds

Material (thickness, in.)	Joint	Laser output (joules)	Pulse length (millisec: half-power)	Joint strength (lb)	Joint resistance (ohms)
0.015 stainless	Butt	8	3.0	21.3	<0.003
	Lap	8	3.0	22.8	<0.003
	Cross	8	3.0	25.0	<0.003
	Tee	8	3.0	23.2	<0.003
0.031 stainless	Butt	10	3.4	31.8	<0.002
	Lap	10	3.4	34.6	<0.002
	Cross	10	3.4	40.0	<0.002
	Tee	11	3.6	40.1	<0.002
0.015–0.031* stainless	Butt	10	3.4	24.3	<0.003
	Lap	10	3.4	24.8	<0.003
	Cross	10	3.4	25.6	<0.003
	Tee	11	3.6	22.0	<0.003
0.015 copper	Butt	10	3.4	5.1	<0.001
	Lap	10	3.4	3.2	<0.001
	Cross	10	3.4	4.3	<0.001
	Tee	11	3.6	3.2	<0.001
0.020 nickel	Butt	10	3.4	12.2	<0.001
	Lap	7	2.8	7.8	<0.001
	Cross	9	3.2	6.8	<0.001
	Tee	11	3.6	12.5	<0.001

Table 6 continued.

0.015 tantalum	Butt	8	3.0	11.5	<0.001
	Lap	8	3.0	8.8	<0.001
	Cross	9	3.2	9.3	<0.001
	Tee	8	3.0	10.8	<0.001
0.025 tantalum	Butt	11	3.5	14.8	<0.001
	Lap	11	3.5	12.9	<0.001
	Tee	11	3.5	17.0	<0.001
0.015/0.25* tantalum	Butt	10	3.4	11.0	<0.001
	Cross	10	3.4	9.2	<0.001
0.015/0.031 stainless	Tee	11	3.6	26.4	<0.001
0.031/0.016 stainless	Tee	11	3.6	19.6	<0.001
0.015/0.025 tantalum	Tee	11	3.6	19.3	<0.001
0.025/0.015 tantalum	Tee	11	3.6	11.4	<0.001
0.015 copper 0.015 tantalum	Butt	10	3.4	3.8	<0.001
0.015 copper 0.015 tantalum	Tee	10	3.4	4.0	<0.001
0.015 copper 0.015 tantalum	Lap	10	3.4	5.3	<0.001
0.015 copper 0.015 tantalum	Cross	10	3.4	4.1	<0.001

*When two wire gauges are used, the upper number in the size designation is the size of the top member of a cross or cross bar of a tee

8

THE LASER IN MEDICINE

DESMOND SMART

International Research and Development Company,
Newcastle upon Tyne

It is to the field of medical physics, and particularly to its application in ophthalmology, that we must turn for some of the more demonstrably valuable applications of the laser. Probably because individual problems were selected for the laser's attention, in contrast to the broader efforts made elsewhere to find a use for the new device, the laser is already well established for certain surgical operations. There is every promise that they will grow steadily in number as physicists and surgeons collaborate to learn more of the consequences when laser light interacts with the different kinds of living tissue. Electromagnetic radiation at or about optical frequencies may yet come to rival the importance of medicine of that radiation of shorter wavelength known as X-rays.

Structure of living tissue

Before discussing the actual and potential applications of lasers in medicine, let us look first at the structure and functions of some living tissues of the body and see how their properties arise. Living tissues can vary markedly in their gross appearance, and differ widely in their function, but it is possible to make some general statements about them — provided, always, that we do not expect every one of these generalizations to apply strictly to every tissue. For a fuller account of the structure and function of various tissues I recommend that references 55, 56 and 57 be consulted.

Essentially, tissues consist of cells and intercellular material. Their structure is largely dependent on the nature of the intercellular material, and their function on the chemical activity of the cells. From one end of the scale to the other, we find in some body fluids a few cells widely separated by quantities of liquid. In some body secretions we may find numbers of cells in very viscous fluids. Then there are the highly cellular organs, such as the brain, with many cells connected together by nerve fibres; and more fibrous material such as muscle. Finally, we find living cells associated with the dense, compact material that forms the bony structures of the body.

A large proportion of the functional characteristics of a tissue derives from the chemical activity of its cells. These cells range in diameter from about 10 to 100 microns. A typical normal cell (Fig. 45) consists of a nucleus, cytoplasm and cell membrane containing various specialized structures. These structures are concerned, along with the cell wall, in the nutrition and respiration of the cell, in its reproductive activity, in producing specialized substances for use out-

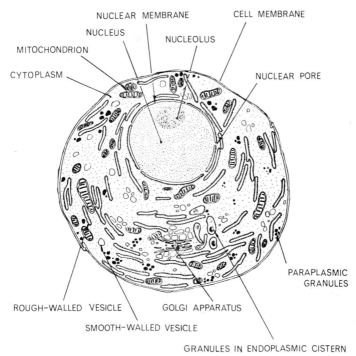

Figure 45   Sketch of a typical cell.

side the cell such as hormones, or in the production of intercellular material to maintain the fabric of the organ as a whole.

This then is but a short list of a host of cell activities, all in their various ways directed to maintaining the whole organism.

Two important chemicals concerned with cell activity are de-oxyribonucleic acids (DNA) and ribonucleic acids (RNA). The DNA tends to be concentrated mainly in the nucleus of the cell, and is often described as the genetic 'code', which confers on daughter cells their proper structure. The RNA, which tends to be found more in the cytoplasm, might also be described as a genetic 'coding' device, but

H   101 one which decides what sort of chemical activity takes place in the cytoplasm.

The organization of cellular activities that may take place in widely separated parts of the body is clearly extremely important. For example, a number of cells may be involved in a process where the body takes something ingested in the normal diet and converts it into a different form. One type of cell will ingest the material and convert it to a different substance, which can be used by a second type of cell — one which could not have dealt with the original material. This process is repeated by the second type of cell, and the material passed along to a third type. This sequence may be repeated many times down the chain until the final chemical form required by some part of the body is achieved.

We can see then how the organization of tissue is related to disease, which is simply a disturbance of cell function.

The first thing we can say is that we would not expect the laser to be able to treat disease where bacteria, viruses or poisons were causing the disturbance, unless the disturbance were very localized and the destruction of the diseased tissue did not matter unduly. However, if we consider a few examples of other types of disease we begin to see where possibilities of treatment arise. As an example, should some change occur in the DNA in the cell (as might be produced by irritation, chemical changes, X-rays, etc), the daughter cell will acquire a structure that differs from that of the parent cell.

Generally speaking, this sort of change is incompatible with the survival of the daughter cell; but occasionally this is not so, and the cell survives and reproduces. It will have lost its specialized function and may multiply rapidly without doing any of the work it would normally undertake. This is the sort of change that can produce a malignant growth. The activities of a cancer cell can be summarized by saying that — like some human beings — it has given up work and concerns itself solely with feeding and reproduction. It is too much to hope that a laser might reverse such a change, but pulses of radiation from a powerful laser may find a place in the treatment of some cancers, as they may destroy the tumour.

Another type of disease is one in which the chemistry of the cytoplasm goes awry, and the tissue produces either too much or too little of a particular secretion. In the first case it is relatively easy to destroy some of the tissue and reduce the secretory activity; but in the second it will be a much more difficult task to stimulate the cell activity. Even this, however, is not beyond the bounds of possibility for it has already been found that some metabolic activities are stimulated by laser radiation. This task will be even more difficult if the cells to be altered are in one of the chain systems I have already mentioned, but nevertheless this may eventually be possible.

Eye surgery

The most successful application at the moment is where we wish to modify tissue and produce a reaction from it. Lasers have found immediate and successful application in surgery, and particularly in

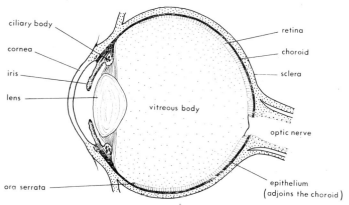

ciliary body
cornea
iris
lens
ora serrata
retina
choroid
sclera
vitreous body
optic nerve
epithelium
(adjoins the choroid)

Figure 46 Section through the human eye.

ophthalmology — treatment of the eye. One particular defect which can arise in the eye is a detachment of the retina from the choroid (see Fig. 46). Normally light incident upon the cornea is focused by the cornea and lens of the eye on to the retina. The retina (Fig. 47) consists of several transparent layers; thus light entering the eye

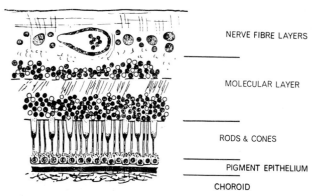

NERVE FIBRE LAYERS

MOLECULAR LAYER

RODS & CONES

PIGMENT EPITHELIUM

CHOROID

Figure 47 Section through the retina.

must pass through these layers to reach the pigmented epithelium of the choroid. The rods and cones in contact with the pigmented epithelium are thereby stimulated, and the nervous impulses they generate travel back through the various retinal layers to the uppermost one. This top layer consists of nerve fibres which conduct the impulses to the point at which the optic nerve enters the eye, and thence to the brain.

It is obvious that with such an arrangement any splitting of the retinal layers, or detachment of the retina from the pigmented epithelium, will interrupt the path for nerve impulses to the brain. The area involved will become blind. If the retina can be flattened against the choroid, however, a re-attachment operation may be attempted; or, if this is not possible, the existing area of the detachment must be sealed off to prevent it progressing to a total detachment.

Essentially, all the procedures used by ophthalmologists aim at producing a localized irritation of the retina and the choroid which will

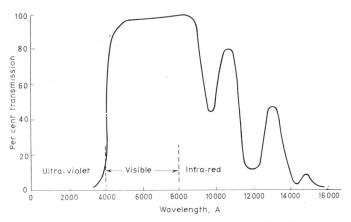

Figure 48 Transmission curve for the clear media of the eye.

result in their cells producing fibrin and forming a small scar. These 'coagulating' techniques are akin to spot welding, and range from a diathermy (hot) needle placed in the spot where the scar is required, to probes cooled by solid carbon dioxide or liquid nitrogen, also used to produce a 'burn' and hence a scar. One technique, developed by Meyer-Schwickerath, raises the temperature of a small part of the retina and choroid to about 85°C. This can be done by directing the light from a powerful xenon arc discharge lamp through a finely focused optical system, to produce a small spot of light on the retina, and thereby a coagulation.

Now if we examine a transmission curve for the clear media of the human eye (Fig. 48) we see the absolute necessity for filters in the light coagulator, to remove all the infrared and ultraviolet radiation, which would otherwise damage the lens and cornea. Since a fair amount of energy, about 4–8 joules, may be required to produce a coagulation, a compromise must be made between the size of lamp which is used, the optics to focus it into the eye, and the size of the scar which is permissible on the retina.

The situation is somewhat different if we use the light from a ruby laser (see Chapter 3). Because it is monochromatic and falls on the

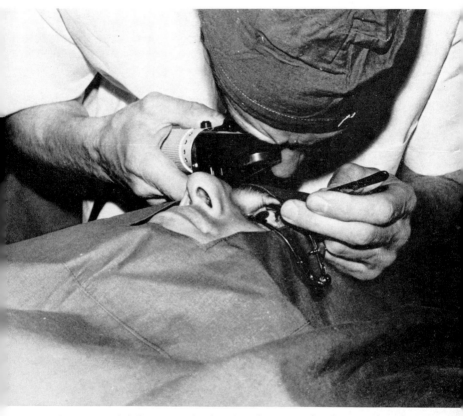

Figure 49 Laser ophthalmoscope developed at the International Research and Development Company, in the hands of a surgeon at Moorfields Eye Hospital, London.

high-transmission part of the curve for the eye's clear media, no filters are necessary. The laser produces a nearly parallel beam of light which can be focused to a very small spot on the retina, or defocused to produce a larger spot if required. Moreover, the coherent nature of the light appears to affect tissue differently from incoherent light, and produces a reaction with much smaller energies (0.1 joule typically) and without large rises in temperature.

105

Laser ophthalmoscope

An experimental laser unit for this purpose has been developed in our laboratories, in collaboration with Mr H. Vernon Ingram and Mr N. Manson of the Royal Victoria Infirmary, Newcastle upon Tyne. This laser ophthalmoscope was used initially in experiments on animals to determine the dose range which would be required to treat patients with retinal detachments. Following this work, a unit was made for clinical trials, consisting of a miniaturized ruby laser small enough to fit in the handle of the usual direct ophthalmoscope. This instrument is small and portable (Fig. 49). The patient need not be anaesthetized; indeed, he need not even be moved to the operating

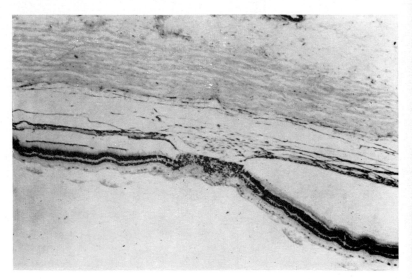

Figure 50 Retinal section, showing the firm adhesion produced by a laser 'spotweld'.

theatre, and many patients have been treated without being moved from their beds in the ward, some even as outpatients.

The reaction is produced by the ruby laser pulse in less than a millisecond, so the patient has no time to react to the bright light and move his eyeball. There is no need, therefore, to fix the eye with forceps or a twist grip, and the patient can co-operate fully and look in the direction required by the surgeon. A section through one of the adhesions or 'spotwelds' produced in this way is shown in Fig. 50. The firmness of the adhesion between the retina (upper portion) and choroid (lower portion) is demonstrated by the way the retina and choroid have separated on either side of the lesion during the cutting of the section. The result of treating a patient (Fig. 51) shows the spotwelds

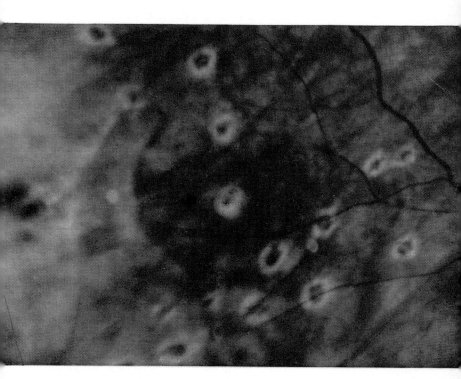

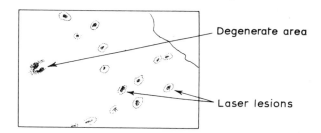

Degenerate area

Laser lesions

Figure 51 Human retina showing generative changes walled off by laser 'spot-welds' to prevent a retinal detachment. (Similar changes in the other eye of this patient had produced a complete detachment.)

surrounding degenerate areas of retina to prevent their producing a detachment, as they had done in the other eye.

Future uses of lasers in ophthalmology may include the treatment of malignant growths in the eye. This will most probably be done using a ruby laser, or a laser operating in the part of the eye's transmission curve having its highest value, since infrared or ultraviolet lasers would cause severe damage to the clear media of the eye. Lasers may also come to be used in the treatment of glaucoma. This is a disease of the eye in which the pressure inside the eye grows too high, and can force the optic nerve out of the back of the eye, rupturing the nerve connection between the retina and the brain. Sometimes the increase in pressure is due to the ciliary body secreting too much fluid, and this sort of case might be treated by using the laser to 'knock out' part of the secretory epithelium of the ciliary body.

Gas lasers may also find a place in ophthalmology, where one might consider their use for various optical measurements on the eye, for checking spectacle or contact lenses quickly or, because of their ability to be focused down to a very small spot, to measure the resolving power of the human retina.

Lasers and the skin

Skin, subcutaneous fat and much connective tissue, such as muscle, are quite transparent to radiation from ruby lasers and from neodymium glass lasers; so much so, in fact, that it is surprising to find these tissues apparently quite unaffected after exposure to high doses of laser energy. The threshold for observable effects on skin or fatty tissue to become apparent immediately is about 25 joules per sq. cm (for ruby); although for dark or negroid skin it can fall to between one-third and one-tenth of this value. This effect of pigmentation on the interaction of the laser beam with tissue is very useful if we consider an attempt to treat certain types of skin disease.

Skin growths ranging from the common wart to a highly malignant melanoma may be treated this way but it is still too early to say whether apparently successful treatments are real cures. Most of the work in this field has been done by Professor Leon Goldman in the USA, but English research groups should soon be reporting their findings. Two of Goldman's cases which have been reported are extremely encouraging. In the first, a man with a highly malignant melanoma of the cheek, which had reached the size of a half a crown, was treated with nine overlapping shots of about 90 joules apiece from a ruby laser. The tumour disintegrated in about ten days and complete healing of the area had taken place in about six weeks. As yet there has been no recurrence or evidence of secondary deposits. In the second, a woman with about 60 secondary deposits from a melanoma had each growth treated separately with a ruby laser and regression of the growths occurred in about a week. In about thirteen months there has been no recurrence of the disease.

It must be emphasized that these results, although valuable, do not promise a panacea for the skin cancers, for out of twenty different types of melanoma tried only seven show marked sensitivity to irradiation by a ruby laser. It may prove possible, of course, to treat other types of tumour with other types of laser operating at quite different wavelengths, but this is by no means certain.

One possibility which is being investigated is the use of dyes which are selectively absorbed by malignant growths. Ideally these should stain malignant tissue almost exclusively, to avoid damage to surrounding tissue, and should have a large absorption band coinciding with the laser's wavelength. Although the situation is reasonable in the visible range it involves a great deal of spectrophotometric work if any of the pulsed infrared lasers are considered.

Apart from skin growths lasers are being considered for the eradication of internal growths, particularly in the lungs, gastro-intestinal tract, the bladder and the urogenital system where as a result surgical exposure of the site of operation may no longer be necessary. The extent to which the approach can be followed up, however, depends largely on the extent to which suitable light guides can be developed. At present the major problem is that energy levels of only 20 joules per sq. cm of light guide will destroy the glass fibres forming the light guide, and the more the light guide is bent the lower is the energy required to produce damage.

Diagnosis by laser?

As regards the use of gas lasers, there are hopes that these may prove quite a valuable adjunct to some of the present methods of diagnosing certain diseases from sections of tissue or from smear preparations. One of the first experiments carried out in IRD's laboratories was to use a helium-neon gas laser to examine specimens of tissue. The images which are observed are rather difficult to relate to normal microscope pictures because they are of a single colour and, as the light is coherent, numerous bright and dark interference fringes are produced. These fringes occur everywhere the tissue changes in thickness or refractive index by an amount equivalent to half a wavelength of the laser light. These images can be used to measure accurately the progress of very slow phenomena such as cell distension or collapse; but, more important, evidence is emerging that some normal and diseased tissues react differently to coherent light, and this could lead to the use of a gas laser in the diagnosis of disease.

Lasers in dentistry

Several attempts have been made to employ lasers in dentistry, an application that might afford great relief to some people as present laser treatments require no anaesthetics. This is due partly to the different way in which a laser works on tissue, for more and more evidence is accumulating that its effects are electromagnetic and not thermal; and partly to the fact that any nerve endings in the focal zone of a laser beam will cease to function about one microsecond after impact. This, of course, is far too fast for cell depolarization to occur—about 1 millisecond—and a nervous impulse to be generated.

An obvious application for the laser, then, is in the removal of caries; the careous area is pigmented and so will absorb sufficient energy to be vaporized, while the white parts of the tooth remain untouched. Another problem which is being tackled is that of fusing filling materials with fairly high melting points to the tooth.

These could have marked advantages as regards wear and also from a cosmetic point of view. Although some of the results have been encouraging, an effective method has not yet been produced. Perhaps the most attractive application of lasers in dentistry will be the fusing over of small fissures in the enamel of the tooth. These fissures are the sites at which caries are most frequently initiated and the value of such treatment may prove high.

9

THE LASER IN TELECOMMUNICATIONS

K. DILLON HARRIS

G. and E. Bradley Limited, London

Ever since its discovery the laser has been considered for use in tele-communications, because of its possibilities in helping to solve some of the perennial problems in this field. Particularly alluring to the engineer are the high coherence and bandwidth of a laser beam, and the simplicity of focusing it.

Bandwidth

The bandwidth of a system determines how much information may be carried by it. As telecommunications have developed over the years, the search for higher and higher channel capacity has lead to the use of increasingly high carrier frequencies. This is because the carrier frequency has to be higher than that of the modulation (otherwise there would be no point in having the carrier) and, practically, the modulation is usually *less* than 10 per cent of the carrier frequency.

A single telegraphy channel using morse code dots and dashes — simply switching the carrier on and off — uses a few hundred cycles of bandwidth. A single telephone channel occupies about 5 Kc/s of bandwidth, because this is the minimum range of frequency which allows different voices to be recognizable; while a 'hi-fi' broadcast will need at least 15 Kc/s to include the full timbre of the orchestral instruments. Frequency modulation (FM) radio uses even more, typically 75 Kc/s. Television in black and white uses several megacycles while colour television needs still more to accommodate the three colour components (red, green and blue), usually making a total of 8 Mc/s when the sound sub-carrier is included.

Thus ordinary radio broadcasts can be accommodated in the bands from 100 Kc/s to 30 Mc/s, although these bands have rapidly become overcrowded with more and more stations, using ever-higher powers, competing for air space. By international agreement the frequency spectrum is divided up into bands and allocated to various users and nations. High-definition television was pioneered by the BBC in Britain in the 1930s, based on 405 lines transmitted at 45 Mc/s in the very high frequency (VHF) region (this continues in Band I). The use of frequency modulation for high-fidelity broadcasting introduced carrier frequencies allocated in the 90 Mc/s band. When Independent Television began to transmit, the first available band was Band III at 210 Mc/s. In all other television services started since the war, higher definition systems have been adopted. North and South America have gone for 525 line systems, while continental Europe has largely standardized on 625 lines, and BBC 2 has followed suit.

These high-definition services and experimental colour transmissions have opened up Bands IV and V in the 400–960 Mc/s region, known as ultra high frequencies (UHF). Higher frequencies still are only slowly being exploited for special broadcasts, such as local educational broadcasts at 4000 Mc/s. These super high frequencies (SHF), which are in fact microwaves, are used mainly for scientific and professional work at the moment — radar, point-to-point link communications and radio astronomy, for example.

Electromagnetic radiation of whatever frequency travels in straight lines in a uniform medium. The natural communication 'over the horizon' obtained with the long, medium and short wavelengths does not contradict this statement. Rather, special circumstances obtain; first, at the ground (a relatively good conductor of electricity) a discontinuity occurs so that the radiation, particularly that of long wavelength, is guided round the curvature of the Earth. For medium and short waves the radiation may also be reflected down from ionized layers in the upper atmosphere, also called the ionosphere, thus covering distances right round the Earth. Frequencies higher than 50 Mc/s are hardly reflected at all by the ionosphere, but still great distances may be covered by VHF and UHF waves, by using sporadic reflection from lower-level ionized layers and by forward scattering; although the power needed for communication by these means is high. Above 1000 Mc/s even these effects become very rare, so that operation may be considered as restricted to line-of-sight.

The development of man-made satellites orbiting the Earth has opened up anew the possibility of using microwaves for communicating over great distances. The success of the *Telstar* and *Relay* satellites has turned the possibility into reality. For communication via a satellite the requirements for reliable operation are to get the maximum power to the satellite, and from the satellite to get the maximum power re-transmitted to the remote ground station. The directivity of an aerial system — that is, the focusing effect in the required direction — improves as the aperture (of the dish for example) increases for radiation of given wavelength, or as the wavelength decreases for constant aperture. Thus higher frequencies help with focusing, so long as the high transmitter power and receiver sensitivity can still be achieved and atmospheric losses do not become greater.

While broadcasting and television requirements are satisfied with up to about 10 Mc/s of bandwidth per channel at the moment, and radars with a similar amount, point-to-point links carrying multi-channel telephone and television circuits require of the order of 100 Mc/s; and the need is continually increasing. The carrier frequencies required for these services have risen steadily over the years — from 2000 Mc/s to 4000 Mc/s, to 6000 and now to 12,000 Mc/s.

Above this last frequency atmospheric losses tend to become important. These losses fluctuate with frequency owing to the various absorption bands of the air and of water vapour molecules. Thus there is a region of poor transmission at 24,000 Mc/s which has to be avoided for propagation through the atmosphere, so that the next useful band occurs at 35,000 Mc/s (8 mm wavelength). Intensive research and development work has been going on for ten years or more to make this and other millimetre-wave bands useful for communications, but success has been limited by the difficulties of generating and detecting these frequencies, and by lack of accurate knowledge of propagation characteristics. Thus far it has been more economical to duplicate circuits of lower frequency.

Laser's immense bandwidth

The advent of the laser opens up immense possibilities. The visible part of the electromagnetic spectrum, tiny though it is (Figure 2) compared with the vast expanses of infrared and ultraviolet on either side, is a 'window' with well-known characteristics. In terms of frequency (rather than the more usual wavelength) it extends from about 400 million to 800 million Mc/s, a band of 400 million megacycles per second — the equivalent of fifty million television channels!

To exploit this vast channel capacity much more than the ability to generate coherent radiation is required. First, one must generate the radiation at sufficient power for the particular purpose. Secondly, one must be able to impress the information required to be transmitted upon the carrier, the process of modulation. Thirdly, the means for propagating the signal from transmitter to distant receiver must be known. And finally, receivers of adequate sensitivity and bandwidth, and capable of demodulating the signal, must be available. Each of these areas has received considerable attention since 1960. Generally speaking, if all of the problems could be solved, and an economical optical communication system be devised, there would be rapid application of these systems, and millimetric and possibly centimetric wave systems would be superseded. However, high-capacity optical systems have still not been devised. To see why we must go in more detail into these problem areas.

Generating the signal

The requirements for the generator of optical radiation for communications purposes are, first, that its frequency shall be correct; secondly, that its power level shall be adequate (1 100 watts of continuous power covers most cases) and able to be sustained; thirdly, that it shall be capable of being modulated; and fourthly, that it shall be reliable, with reasonable life, running costs, etc.

Early lasers all failed to meet one or more of these needs. The ruby lasers produced visible red output at high peak power (kilowatts to megawatts) but only for short bursts, modulation was difficult and reliability was low. The helium-neon gas lasers produced visible red output continuously but at relatively low power (milliwatts), and their life was short. Gallium arsenide semi-conductor lasers gave reasonable peak powers (tens of watts) pulse-modulated, but required liquid nitrogen cooling to do so, and oscillated in the near-infrared where detector sensitivity was much reduced compared with the visible region. The general poor efficiency of lasers (a few per cent overall at best) is no great disadvantage, however, because microwave transmitters of similar characteristics are little better.

Developments of the three basic types of laser (see Chapters 3 and 4) have led to marked improvements, particularly in gas lasers, which always seemed to have greatest chance of success for this application. This is because they are the closest approach to conventional generators of lower frequency, with a continuous output and greatest spectral purity. Lasers using various gases or mixtures of gases are now working from the blue part of the spectrum (0.4 micron wavelength) using argon gas, through the green (0.5 micron), yellow and orange (argon and krypton), to the red (0.6 micron) and near-infrared (1.15 and 3.39 microns), with helium-neon; and recently to 10 microns using a mixture of carbon dioxide and nitrogen gases. The argon and carbon dioxide/nitrogen systems have given more than 10 and 100 watts of continuous output respectively, while the helium-neon system has produced 1 watt. Of the two most powerful sources to date, argon, working in the green, is most favourably placed with respect to the optimum sensitivity of photoelectric detectors. The carbon dioxide/nitrogen system, although not so well placed with regard to atmospheric absorption, is particularly interesting because its efficiency is high, which will help the achievement of 1 kW or more of continuous power. There are sensitive and fast-response detectors of the photo-conductive kind for use at 10 microns, but they need cooling to liquid helium temperature ($4°K$).

The reliability and life of gas lasers has also improved vastly over the last few years (Chapter 3). With low-power helium-neon types, on which most development work has been done so far, lives of several thousand hours are now quite normal. With the new high-power types of gas laser more work has still to be done, but one can confidently expect lives of more than 1000 hours in the near future.

Modulating the signal

In order to impress information on a light beam for communications it is necessary to have an adequate system for modulating the beam. The simplest type of modulation is amplitude modulation, produced either by varying a parameter of the light transmitter itself and so changing the emission amplitude in a periodic way, or by interposing a modulating element in the beam after its emission from the generator.

With a gas laser, for instance, simply by varying the input power to the plasma column over a small range, we can obtain depths of modulation up to about 10 per cent with an audio signal. The disadvantages of this method are, first, that this small depth of modulation makes inefficient use of the carrier power; and secondly, that the bandwidth obtainable is limited by the bandwidth of the electrode system coupling to the plasma. This limitation means that, at the moment bandwidths up to 1 Mc/s are achieved easily, and up to 100 Mc/s with increasing difficulty.

External modulation may be achieved by devices using electro-optically active materials. Such materials, when activated by an electric field, rotate the plane of polarization of a light beam travelling through them. Best-known of such devices is the Kerr cell, which consists of a glass-walled cell containing highly purified nitrobenzene. It is provided with two parallel metal electrodes, like a primitive capacitor. The light beam is transmitted between these plates in a parallel beam. Rotation of the plane of polarization is proportional to the voltage across the electrodes. In order to turn the variation in polarization angle into an amplitude variation, a fixed polarization analyser must follow the Kerr cell.

This type of modulation is quite useful, being limited in bandwidth mainly by the capacitance of the electrodes and the inconveniently high modulation voltages (typically 10–20 kV); and, more seriously, by the high light loss resulting from the combination of cell and analyser. The efficiency of present lasers is so low, a few per cent at most, that further loss in the modulator is obviously most undesirable. Bandwidths up to 10,000 Mc/s have been achieved with the solid versions (Pockel cells), using such crystals as ammonium dihydrogen phosphate (ADP). This material has high electro-optical activity, so requiring less material and lower voltages, so that smaller structures, more suitable for extremely high modulation frequencies, can be realized.

115

Recently, other more promising modulators have been investigated using piezoelectric effects and modulation effects within the atoms of the laser material itself. More work on these is urgently needed before they become completely satisfactory.

Transmission systems

Once having obtained the modulated laser beam it is necessary to convey it with minimum loss of information and quality to the remote receiver. Broadly, this may be done in two ways: by *free propagation* or by *guided propagation*.

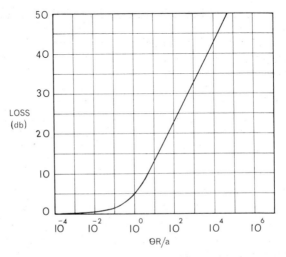

Figure 52   Curve showing the transmission loss between two telescopes.

In a free propagation system, the radiation is launched towards the receiver after being processed by a telescope (the optical equivalent of an aerial) to give as high a directivity as is practicable. The larger the aperture of the telescope, the better the focusing, subject to the mechanical accuracy of the telescope lens or mirror being maintained. But as the aperture increases beyond a few feet the cost rises rapidly. In practice, focusing of laser beams to between 10 and 100 seconds of arc can be attained with reasonable care without going to apertures greater than a few feet. The ideal system for free propagation would be for the transmitted beam to fall completely within the aperture of another telescope at the receiving end. It cannot be achieved economically, except over short ranges, but the effects of the inverse square law can be offset quite effectively.

Fig. 52 shows the loss between two telescopes of equal aperture,

116

diameter a. The loss is seen to be kept very low out to a distance R between telescopes, of the order of a/θ, where θ is the divergence angle of the transmitted beam. For $\theta = 10^{-4}$ radians and $a = 1$ metre, $R \sim 10$ km. Since the beam focusing achievable depends, owing to diffraction effects, on the wavelength of the radiation and the aperture of the transmitting telescope, as $\theta \sim \lambda/a$, another way of expressing the distance for low loss is $R \sim a^2/\lambda$.

This formula shows clearly the advantage that optical wavelengths have compared with radio and microwave wavelengths. For comparable apertures, the wavelengths and thus the distances are in the

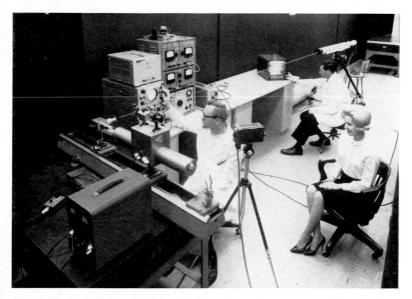

Figure 53   Experiments in the use of a laser beam in deep-space voice and video communications, at North American Aviation, USA.

ratio 100,000:1 at least. To be fair to microwaves, much larger apertures have been constructed for them than for optical telescopes; compare Jodrell Bank's radio telescope at 250 ft with the Mount Palomar telescope's 200 inches. Even taking this (perhaps temporary) difference into account, there remains a factor of 1000 in favour of optical wavelengths.

When we come to consider the effects of loss within the transmission medium, the position is more complex. The fact that our eyes have evolved to operate in the 'visible' region of the electromagnetic spectrum points to this region being good, all round, for transmission purposes in the atmosphere of the Earth: a true 'window', with regions having less desirable characteristics close by on either

117

J

side. Unfortunately this 'window' is much affected by the weather, fog being the worst offender but rain, snow, and so on, also producing serious reduction in transmission. Whereas the animal world, including man himself, has always put up with curtailed performance in such conditions, communication systems cannot be permitted to be out of action for even a small percentage of the time. This imposes another condition on optical systems which affects their economics: either much greater transmitter power has to be available to overcome bad weather, or the distance covered has to be reduced and the number of repeater stations increased proportionately.

Guided propagation is an alternative method of transmission which could overcome the problem of bad-weather absorption of the signal. Here the light is transmitted through a rod of transparent material or along the inside of a pipe, or else it is refracted by a succession of components which continually refocus the beam. Fibre optics and 'light-pipes' have been known and used for many years for ducting light over short distances; they are a very useful way of feeding light in and out of confined spaces, and round bends. At microwave frequencies pipes or 'waveguides' have also been used widely over short distances, and have been investigated extensively for long-distance communications. But so far as microwaves are concerned, the high-cost of the waveguide has defeated guided propagation so far.

Devices of the same type are being investigated, however, for optical communications (Fig. 53). Several features now look more favourable: for example, the smallness of the wavelength means that the cross-section of the guide can be as small as can conveniently be handled. Fog and other adverse conditions can be excluded completely, of course. The main problem will be the attainment of low propagation loss.

When one gets outside the Earth's atmosphere the case for communications at optical frequencies becomes more straightforward. Already experiments have been carried out from Earth to manned spacecraft. The principal advantage comes from the small size and weight of the transmission equipment, which can easily be carried by spacecraft. A disadvantage, on the other hand, will be the difficulty of tracking very small targets with such very narrow beams.

The recent extension of laser action into the far-infrared and sub-millimetre regions of the spectrum between the visible and the microwave bands may bring about further changes in our thinking on optical communications. The most interesting development in this connection has been the operation, at a wavelength of 337 microns (approximately 1 million Mc/s, or 1 teracycle), of a gas laser using the cyanide (CN) radical. This wavelength occurs within another 'window' in the atmospheric absorption curve, and also has the ability to penetrate fog considerably better than visible light.

Sub-millimetre lasers are already being studied for telecommunications purposes. Fig. 54 shows a commercial sub-millimetre source which generates pulses of greater than 1 watt of peak power at up to 50 pulses a second.

Reception of the signal

Having collected whatever fraction of the transmitted signal is possible by a telescope at the receiving station, we must amplify and demodulate it to extract the original information. The simplest optical receiver is the photocell, or its semiconductor equivalent, the photo-transistor, which converts light energy into electric current. The photomultiplier is the most sensitive device of this type, combining the features of a photocell and high-gain amplifier in one envelope.

Figure 54 The sub-millimetre (337-micron) maser developed at the National Physical Laboratory and manufactured by G. and E. Bradley.

One very good light receiver consists of an optical system which focuses the incident light on to the cathode of a photomultiplier tube, having first passed it through a narrow band filter to reject light of unwanted wavelengths. Nearly all laser communications systems have used this type of receiver up to now. Demodulation takes place in the phototube automatically because, although it responds to the energy of the light, it will not respond to the periodicity of the light. Thus the only variations in amplitude remaining in the electric current from the tube are those impressed on the light as modulation. The limitation in bandwidth amounts to about 100 Mc/s, although special tubes have been made having more than 1000 Mc/s bandwidth. This imposes a limit to the amount of modulation which can be received of course.

To make full use of the capacity of a laser beam it will be necessary to go to very great bandwidths in receivers, as in modulators. Following radio practice one would expect the superheterodyne method to prove useful, and this turns out to be the case. In such a system the incoming signal is made to beat with a locally generated signal of nearly, but not exactly the same frequency in a non-linear device, so that a difference frequency is produced. This 'intermediate frequency' is then amplified by conventional electronic techniques and demodulated. For example, the intermediate frequency could be a microwave one, say at 10,000 Mc/s, which has a bandwidth of perhaps 1000 Mc/s itself. This band could be occupied by many television signals and speech signals, which could be separated by multi-branch filters, and each channel converted down in frequency again by heterodyning, before being processed normally. Such systems have been demonstrated successfully in the laboratory.

The non-linear device required for the superheterodyne mixing of light may be a photo-cathode or any of a number of optically active materials such as have been described in connection with modulators. The most practical type of mixer operating at the moment is the photo travelling wave tube. This is a cross between a photomultiplier and the microwave amplifier called a travelling wave tube. In such a tube a window allows the incoming light signal and a local signal both to be focused on to a cathode surface. Electrons are given off by the cathode in response to the stimulating light and, since the process is non-linear, the electron beam has a component wave impressed on it of a frequency equal to the difference between the input signal and the local oscillator signal. The electron beam is focused inside a wire wound in the form of a helix. Interaction between electric currents in the wire and the beam leads to the difference frequency being amplified as it travels along the helix, until it is coupled out for use.

Optical radar

The other main branch of telecommunications is radar — the measurement of distance and location by electromagnetic radiation. Dr Rowley (Chapter 10) discusses the measurement of short distances by optical means; here we are concerned chiefly with distances of a few to many miles.

There are basically three ways in which a laser may be used as the source of energy in distance measurement. In all these methods the light is transmitted to a reflecting or diffusing surface and back to a receiver near the transmitter. The differences occur in the way the light is used in the space between. These three ways are:

1. By using the high coherence of the laser output to produce an interference pattern over the distance to be measured, it is possible to express the distance in terms of a number of wavelengths of light.

2. By modulating the laser with some high-frequency radio signal it is possible to compare the phase of the modulation of the transmitted wave with that of the received wave, and so calculate the distance.

3. A pulse-modulated signal may be timed over the distance and back so that, knowing the velocity of light, the distance can be computed.

The devices for producing the radiation, for modulating, transmitting and receiving it for these purposes are closely similar, if not identical, to those used for communicating. But there are special features which need to be examined in detail.

Measurement by optical interference

Optical interference has been used for many years in the measure ments of length. Examples range from the determination of the metre in terms of wavelengths of light to the use of moiré fringes in machine tool control. These systems consist usually of two surfaces which are illuminated with incoherent light to set up a three-dimensional standing wave pattern between the surfaces. Viewed from outside, light and dark fringes are seen, which indicate positions where the path differences between the light reaching adjacent fringes are half a wavelength.

A simple example is the Fabry-Perot interferometer, which consists basically of two partially silvered parallel mirrors. Parallel monochromatic light entering the space between the mirrors through one mirror is reflected back and forth between them many times. Interference occurs between these multiple rays so that, viewed through a telescope by transmission or reflection, a concentric system of ring fringes is seen. The diameter of the rings is dependent on the wavelength of the light and the distance between the two mirrors. On changing the separation, the fringe pattern expands or contracts. Movement of half a wavelength shifts the pattern by one fringe: changes of 1/10 fringe or 0.000003 cm are readily detectable, so that we see the Fabry-Perot cell is a very sensitive indicator of change of length.

In order to measure distance we need the number of complete half-wavelengths between the two mirrors and the fraction over. The fraction may be calculated from measurements of the pattern. The integer may be found by repeating the experiment with other wavelengths of light. This is the so-called method of exact fractions.

The usefulness of the interference method depends on the visibility of the fringes, or how clear and sharp they are. With increasing separation between the two mirrors more and more light is required to be beamed into the cell to maintain good visibility. With conventional sources to get more light the lamp has to be run hotter or has to be bigger, or both. The former makes focusing of the light into the interferometer more difficult, while the latter broadens the emission line, which also degrades the fringe pattern. Thus, this system was limited practically to distances of a few tens of centimetres.

The replacement of the lamp by a laser produces a marked improvement in the distance over which good quality fringes may be obtained. A simple gas laser giving a few milliwatts of output power gives good fringes over distances of tens of metres (see Chapter 10). The combination of coherence, narrow linewidth and high directivity gives the laser this advantage. The limit to the distance which can be measured is set by atmospheric disturbances which affect the fringe visibility.

Apart from the use of a laser simply as an improved light source, further improvements result if automatic readout systems are required. The realization of precise distance measuring equipment of this type is being sought in several different directions. First, in the machine tool field there is still a great need for micrometers which can measure the dimensions being machined continuously, and so allow a correction for tool wear to be fed to the tool. Here it is not primarily the microinch accuracy which is attractive, but the ease with which the laser may be fitted into an automatic system. Secondly, in the fields of marine, power and aeronautical engineering there is a need of equipment for accurately mapping the contours of large parts such as propellers, turbine blades, fuselage and wing sections. These measurements may require accuracies of the order of a thousandth of an inch in distances of over 10 feet, with lateral scanning to plot continuously the contour under test. Thirdly, in civil engineering the increasing need for precise construction of large structures is putting a considerable strain on existing methods of surveying. Examples of such structures include platforms for large generating plant and nuclear reactors; dams, bridges and tunnels; and radio telescopes and particle accelerators. These projects are already demanding measurement to less than a millimetre of distances of the order of 100 metres often as changes in length.

All these applications can use a single wavelength laser and fringe counting methods. The development of practical devices in these fields is being carried out in many laboratories, the main problems to be solved concern the lasers themselves, to produce compact and reliable ones which have the required stability of output, and low running costs.

Measurement by modulated beam

Existing equipment for distance measurements uses either a coherent microwave signal derived from a valve source such as a klystron, or an incoherent light source such as a filament lamp or arc tube. The former type is easy to modulate at frequencies up to 100 Mc/s and can be used over very long distances with a simple directive aerial and a sensitive, selective superheterodyne receiver. It is not seriously affected by weather conditions. On the other hand, the beam spreads sufficiently to give spurious reflections on occasions, which make the distance readings ambiguous. Modulation at higher frequencies to increase the accuracy becomes increasingly difficult and expensive and is, of course, limited by the frequency of the generator itself. At a modulation frequency of 100 Mc/s, with phase comparison accurate to 1 degree, distance can be measured accurately to about 1 centimetre.

The existing optical systems, being incoherent, suffer generally from poor signal-to-noise ratio, particularly in daylight, and from the difficulty of modulation at very high frequencies. The laser offers improvements to the optical system to bring it up to the standard of the microwave system; in other words, the high spectral intensity allows receiver sensitivity to be improved by the addition of narrow band interference filters, so discriminating against unwanted light. The nature of laser light makes modulation up to at least 10 million Mc/s feasible in time. The beam spread from a laser transmitter is considerably less than that from a conventional light source, or from a microwave aerial of comparable size. To obtain full advantage from this high angular discrimination, however, careful alignment of the system is required.

Its advantages should make the laser a most useful component in distance measuring equipment for surveying and geodesy. The limitation due to atmospheric absorption may be overcome by using wavelengths (in the far-infrared for example) where the loss due to water vapour can be less than with visible light. The development of modulation systems based on lasers is, as with other laser communication systems, dependent on the availability of suitably rugged, long-life devices. Such devices, as we have seen, are now becoming available.

Measurement by radar

By sending out pulses of light and collecting the diffused echoes with a telescope feeding a photomultiplier, it is possible to extend the techniques of radar for distance measurements into the optical region. The first requirement from a laser for such a system is high peak power, in order to get useful range information off diffuse targets. Pulsed ruby lasers meet this requirement if one-pulse, or at least low pulse repetition rate, is an acceptable mode of operation.

Within a few months of the operation of the first ruby laser a simple range-finding set-up was tested. This system had to be improved considerably before widespread use could be made of it. The main modification was to the form of the output pulse of the laser.

In an unmodified ruby laser, the output occurs as a random succession of spikes lasting for a time of the order of a millisecond (Chapter 3). The height and position of the spikes is quite different from shot to shot. This makes recognition of the echo pulse difficult if it is weak; also precise measurement of the elapsed time very difficult, particularly if done electronically with a high-frequency clock.

Schemes to produce single pulses from ruby lasers have therefore been investigated intensively. The technique of Q-switching has proved very successful in this connection. This uses some means of frustrating the normal operation of the laser until the populations of the atomic states have been inverted, and then releasing all the stored energy suddenly, which produces a very high intensity of output in a very short time.

The means of achieving Q-switching may commonly be mechanical, electro-optical or chemical. An example of a mechanical Q-switch is a rotating prism used as one of the end reflectors of the laser optical resonator. Careful timing of the excitation discharge to the rotation of the prism holds up the emission of laser radiation until the prism is square with the end of the ruby rod, when emission occurs rapidly. Typical results are an increased peak power of more than 1000 times in a pulse duration of about 20 nanoseconds, for a rotation speed of 30,000 rpm.

The most common electro-optical Q-switch uses a Kerr cell with suitable polarizers. With the polarizers initially crossed to heavily attenuate the transmission of light through the ruby, the ruby is excited by the usual discharge from a flash tube. The Kerr cell is then pulsed to rotate the plane of polarization so that the transmission attenuation disappears. Sudden laser output occurs, with typically up to a thousand times the peak power lasting perhaps 10 nanoseconds.

The chemical Q-switch, the most recent addition to the devices at our disposal, consists of a simple cell of liquid which is a solution of a bleachable dye. Popular examples of such dyes are phthalo- and crypto-cyanine. These dyes normally absorb heavily in the red part of the spectrum, but under high intensity of light abruptly become transparent. Such a cell placed in the optical resonator of a laser has the same effect as a Kerr cell, but one which operates automatically under the influence of the laser light itself. The beauty of this device is its simplicity, no power supplies or timing devices being necessary. The disadvantage is that one has little control over the point at which the pulse comes within the time when the laser material is excited. However, this does not matter for static distance measurement.

The accuracy to which measurement of distance can be made using the pulse radar method depends, first, on the rise of the trans-

mitted pulse, and secondly, on the amount of sophisticated electronics that can be accommodated in the equipment. As present
Q-switched lasers have pulse rise times of about 10 nanoseconds, the
limiting accuracy of distances measured is about 3 metres. This can
probably be improved by a factor of 10 in time, but only at the price
of considerable complication in both laser and electronics. Thus,
this method is not a high-precision one for surveying on the ground.
Its main use comes from the fact that measurements can be made
single-ended, using the back-scattered light off buildings, trees and

Figure 55 Portable range-finder for
surveying, which weighs only 28 lb.
developed by G. and E. Bradley.

Figure 56 Large range-finder equipped with a 12-in. reflecting telescope,
developed by G. and E. Bradley.

almost any object which may be discerned by looking through a
telescope. Thus the first main use has been military, but it seems
probable that surveyors will also find use for this type of instrument
in remote areas where travel is difficult. A portable laser range-
finder is shown in Fig. 55. This equipment has a total weight of 28 lb,
including battery, and shows the advanced state of development
which has been reached.

For distance measurement upwards into the air the radar method
using lasers is proving very useful. At distances from 50 to 5000
metres, cloud height and structure can be determined with sufficient
accuracy for meteorological purposes. Atmospheric phenomena
such as inversion layers and clear air turbulence (CAT) have also

been detected with laser systems. Satellite tracking experiments are being carried out successfully by several groups. In this application, the distance is so large that the accuracy, to a few metres, is very high. These experiments have great relevance to the future of geodesy, of course, for measuring distances beyond the horizon. Fig. 56 shows a larger range-finder developed for this type of work, based on a 12-inch reflecting telescope. The laser develops 500 MW of peak power in each pulse.

10

THE LASER IN MEASUREMENT AND CONTROL

Dr W. R. C. ROWLEY
National Physical Laboratory, Teddington

Soon after the first lasers had been demonstrated, their possibilities in length measurement were realized and simple measuring devices were constructed. Since the early days lasers have developed considerably, and so also have the techniques for employing them in measuring instruments. In some cases a laser may be used in place of a more conventional light source in order to extend the range of an instrument or perhaps to make it easier to use. Of greater interest are the applications in which advantage can be taken of the remarkable features of laser radiation to develop techniques which were hitherto inconvenient or impossible.

Much of the development of laser measurement technique has been directed towards their use in one way or another for the measurement of length. The term 'length' in this context includes not only the measurement of physical objects such as standard length bars, but also the measurement, on the one hand, of distances of several miles and, at the other extreme, of minute changes of distance, such as those involved in seismology. Important laser techniques also include measurements of refractive index, velocity, angle and the rate of angular rotation.

The three main categories of laser — gas, solid-state, and semiconductor — each have their own sphere of application. The high power of the pulsed doped crystal laser lends itself particularly to radar-like techniques in long-distance work, for which the absorption of the atmosphere is a limitation. The semiconductor laser has been applied in a similar way, although because of its lower peak power the range is more restricted than that of the doped crystal device. The compensating advantages are its smaller physical size, high repetition rate and good electrical efficiency. The gas laser, on the other hand, has shown itself to be useful in a variety of ways and has opened the door to some exciting new techniques. In view of its versatility it is appropriate to consider first some of these techniques applicable to the gas laser.

Interferometry with lasers

The properties of the radiation from a gas laser which distinguish it most from other sources are that the light is almost purely mono-chromatic and coherent (see Chapter 2); these are properties which make the laser particularly attractive as a source for interferometric measurements. With conventional light sources, even the most pure of the so-called monochromatic radiations has in fact a significant spread of wavelength. It is this wavelength spread which has pre-viously restricted the use of interferometry to quite short distances. One of the best of the discharge tube sources is the krypton-86 lamp, which emits the radiation by which the metre is defined; but even with this source it is extremely difficult to measure interferometrically over a distance as great as one metre. But with a gas laser the spread of wavelength can be so much less — a factor of 10^6 or 10^8 is in-volved — that the source no longer restricts the distance over which interferometry may be used.

Although the narrow bandwidth of laser radiation is one of its most important features, it has other properties which are advan-tageous in interferometry. For example, most interferometers re-quire parallel or nearly parallel light. Normally this is derived from an incoherent light source by imaging the source on to a pinhole or slit which is at the focus of a lens. But inevitably only a small pro-portion of the available light can be effectively utilized. The beam of light emitted by a gas laser operating in a single axial mode can, however, be made almost perfectly parallel by a simple lens system without using either slit or pinhole, so that none of the emitted light need be lost. The increase of illumination realized in practice can be very marked. This is of great importance, in that photo-electric observation techniques become much simpler and more rapid.

Techniques for the measurement of engineering length standards — slip gauges and end bars — are well-established, and I do not pro-pose to consider them here. Certainly a laser can be used as the source for one of these instruments in order to increase the bright-ness of the fringe pattern and to make possible the measurement of longer gauges; but the laser can be better employed in interferometers especially designed for it. The usual gauge interferometer is essen-tially a static instrument, relying upon visual observation of the fringes in light of several colours. The laser, however, has sufficient intensity to enable dynamic measurements to be made — it can measure a moving object or monitor a changing length. This is a task which can be done only at minutely slow speeds with conven-tional light sources, but which the laser performs easily.

It is in this kind of measurement, the measurement of change of distance, that the laser interferometer has most to offer. It consider-ably widens the scope of interferometric measurement and makes it suitable, for example, for monitoring the position of the carriage of a travelling microscope or perhaps a machine tool, particularly in applications where unusually high accuracy is required.

Interferometer design

The special properties of the gas laser can lead to considerable simplifications in the optical arrangement of interferometers. A particularly elegant system originated in the Services Electronics Research Laboratory. The basic arrangement, shown in Fig. 57, uses only one plane mirror in addition to the laser. Light is reflected from this mirror back into the laser. If the distance to this external mirror is such that the returned light, when it passes into the laser, is in phase with the main laser wave, then it increases the strength of this wave. If, on the other hand, it should be in the opposite phase, then the laser's intensity is reduced. Thus when the external mirror is moving towards, or away from, the laser its optical distance alters continuously and the returned beam goes periodically in and out of phase. This causes the whole laser intensity to vary.

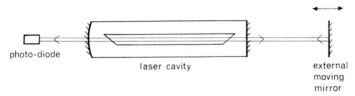

Figure 57　Basic arrangement of the SERL laser interferometer.

The effect on the intensity can be very strong, even if the external mirror reflects only a small fraction of the light. A movement of half a wavelength results in a complete cycle of the intensity variation, so that for the red line of a helium-neon laser successive maxima of intensity correspond to a movement of roughly 12 micro-inches. By detecting these variations photo-electrically, and counting them electronically, the movement and position of the mirror can be followed very precisely. The maximum speed of movement which can be employed with this simple system is limited by the maximum modulation rate of the laser, which corresponds, however, to several inches per second.

Apart from indicating how far the mirror has moved, this device also indicates how fast it is moving. The counting rate is a direct measure of mirror velocity. This follows, of course, because it measures how far the mirror has gone in a certain time, but it can also be argued from another standpoint. One can regard the light reflected from the moving mirror as having its frequency shifted by doppler effect. When this shifted frequency is mixed again with the original, one gets a beat signal at the difference frequency — a frequency identical to the interferometer's counting rate.

As a velocity measuring device, the laser interferometer, either in the special form I have just described or in a more normal configuration, has certain useful properties. No mechanical contact with the moving object is necessary and it can be used either to give a very accurate answer (correct to one part in a million or better) or to give modest accuracy over a very short time interval.

As an example, consider an interferometer using the helium-neon red line, with an electronic timing system based on a 1 Mc/s oscillator. With an object moving at one foot per second (corresponding to a doppler shift of 1 Mc/s), a velocity reading, correct to 1 per cent, could be obtained in 100 microseconds, during which time the object would have moved only 0.0012 inches. For a higher accuracy a proportionately greater time and distance would be necessary.

The interferometer system which I have described is an example of an arrangement developed specifically for the laser. Apart from its simplicity it has the valuable feature that it is practically unaffected by stray light in the measuring path. The laser acts as a selective detector, responding only to light within its narrow spectral range, so that it is scarcely affected by white light sources. Hence the arrangement has found application in the measurement of refractive index changes in a glowing gas,[58] where interferometry would normally be impossible. This interferometer system is not, however, ideal for all applications. In particular, it is not easily adapted, in the general case, to the measurement of bi-directional movements.

One of the best-known types of interferometer must surely be the Michelson interferometer. In his classic measurement of the metre in terms of the wavelength of the red line of cadmium, Michelson himself in 1892 used the technique of counting interference fringes. With J. R. Benoit, he measured a 0.3 mm intermediate standard by slowly moving one of the interferometer mirrors whilst counting by eye the number of fringes which passed — more than a thousand in this case. With photo-electric detectors and electronic counters the drudgery can be taken out of fringe counting, but until the introduction of the laser the counting rate was restricted to a few hundred counts per second by the feeble brightness of monochromatic sources.

When used with a laser source the optical system may be simplified, as shown in Fig. 58. There is no need for a small pinhole in order to get parallel light, and the beam can be reduced to a diameter of a few millimetres without any loss of light. Also the reference mirror can be put much closer to the beam splitter since it is no longer necessary to keep the path difference small. Indeed, the reference mirror may be incorporated with the beam splitter in a single unit.

With the usual arrangement of the Michelson interferometer there is a complementary beam, in addition to the normal output beam, which is directed back into the source. Normally this is unimportant, but with a laser source it can give rise to confusing modulations of the laser intensity. The unwanted beam can be suppressed by optical means, such as a quarter-wave plate and polarizer inserted between

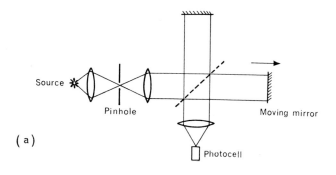

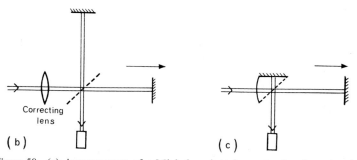

Figure 58 (*a*) Arrangement of a Michelson interferometer for photoelectric fringe counting. (*b*) With a laser light source, the lens system is simplified and the beam diameter reduced. (*c*) The semi-reflector and reference mirror may be combined in a single unit with the correcting lens.

laser and interferometer; but it may alternatively be turned to advantage.

By a modification of the interferometer this beam can be arranged to fall to one side of the source, as in Fig. 59(a). With a normal dielectric coated semi-reflector the interference signals at the detectors A and B will be in antiphase (one beam being light whilst the other is dark). Thus both detectors can be used together in a balanced amplifier system, giving an improved signal-to-noise ratio.

A variation of this interferometer arrangement, which has been used at the National Physical Laboratory, is illustrated in Fig. 59(b). The mirror in the reference beam has been eliminated and separate semi-reflectors are used for dividing and recombining the beams. This layout gives a wider separation between input and output beams. The reference beam goes directly between the semi-reflectors and follows a significantly shorter path than that of the variable beam, so that this arrangement is unsuitable for use with conventional light sources.

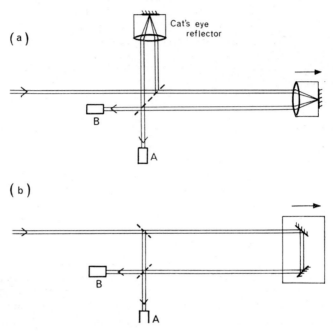

Figure 59 (*a*) Michelson interferometer with 'cat's eye' reflectors, so that no light is reflected back into the source. The two photocells may be used with a bi-directional counter. (*b*) Alternative arrangement, used in a measuring machine at the National Physical Laboratory.

The straightforward Michelson interferometer and its derivatives can quite easily be made direction sensitive. The output signals are sinusoidal in character and the direction of movement may be determined from two such signals if they have a phase shift of roughly 90 degrees between them. These two signals can be handled by the input circuitry of a bi-directional electronic counter so as to automatically add the counts when the movement is in one direction, and subtract them for the reverse movement.

There need be no ambiguity in this kind of system, which will deal with rapid and random changes of direction, such as those caused by vibration. This type of bi-directional counting is indeed widely used in connection with moiré-fringe, metrological gratings for machine tool control, and other applications.

In the case of an interferometer, the two-phase shifted signals can be derived in several ways. One method is to put a small step across half of one of the mirrors, or to insert a stepped plate into one beam, so the two halves of the beam aperture have path lengths which differ by an odd multiple of a quarter of a wavelength. The two sections of the output beam are then arranged to fall on separate detectors. The objection to this system is that division into two beams of approximately semi-circular cross-section becomes inconvenient when the diameter is only one or two millimetres, as may well be the case in a laser interferometer.

An alternative approach is to change the phase difference between the signals from detectors A and B (Fig. 59(a) and (b)), so that it becomes 90 degrees. This can be done by putting a quarter-wave plate into either the variable or the reference beam, and orientated at 45 degrees to the plane of polarization. With a polarizer in front of each detector the required phase shift can be introduced. It has also been shown[59] that appropriate coating of the semi-reflector can achieve a similar result without using the extra optical components, whilst at the same time giving an improved transmission of light.

Application of laser interferometry

The laser interferometer forms quite a versatile system of measurement in that it is applicable to a wide range of distances, from a fraction of an inch up to at least several hundred feet. Whilst being capable of making length measurements of the highest precision it is nevertheless quite rapid in operation. Apart from fringe-counting interferometry, the laser may be used in static or semi-static systems for the measurement of long distances, or small changes of long distances. For example it has been proposed for the measurement of earth movements over geological faults. There are also possible applications in surveying for those special situations where unusually high accuracy is demanded, as in the case of the construction of the large particle accelerating machines which play so important a part in modern physics.

The signals from a fringe-counting interferometer are very similar to those of a moiré-fringe grating system, in which a long diffraction grating in conjunction with a short one to give a sinusoidal variation of transmitted light as one grating moves relative to the other. The advantage of the laser interferometer is that it gives a much finer scale and is inherently more accurate.

133

Whereas the diffraction grating system relies for its accuracy upon the perfection of spacing of the grating graduations, the interferometer measures in terms of the wavelength of the laser light, which

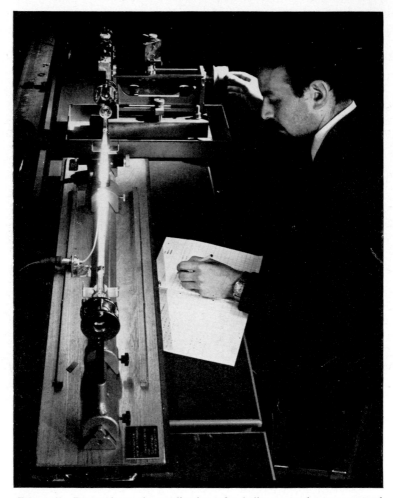

Figure 60   Research on the application of a helium-neon laser to control a machine tool's movements to within half a wavelength of red light, at Elliott-Automation's laboratories.

can be kept substantially constant. The accuracy of the wavelength scale, using a stabilized laser, can be one part in a hundred million or better — an accuracy which far surpasses normal requirements.

In practice, the accuracy of measurement with a laser interferometer is limited by the design of the measuring apparatus and uncertainties about the temperature of the object under measurement. Nevertheless the high potential accuracy makes the system attractive to the standards laboratory and for industrial calibrating apparatus. Probably the interferometer will also find use directly on a machine tool (see Figs 60 and 61), to take over from the moiré-fringe grating and similar techniques, but it is uncertain at this stage to what extent it will offer economic advantages.

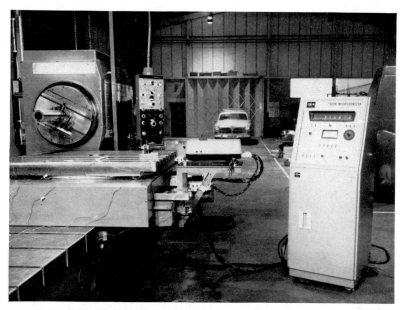

Figure 61 Laser interferometer developed by Cutler-Hammer, USA, used to calibrate the digital position readout equipment on a machine tool under development at the Churchill Group's research centre. The interferometer has an absolute accuracy of one part in two million.

A disadvantage of the laser interferometer is that the unit of measurement, half the wavelength of the light, is not an exact engineering unit. For the red light of the helium laser, for example, it is 12.5 micro-inches; but not exactly so. The precise value depends in any case upon the temperature and pressure of the air at the time of measurement. This is not of great concern in many applications where the results can be calculated some time after measurement, but it can be an annoying complication. Where a direct display of the measured distance is essential, a small computer has been combined with the electronic counting system to perform the transformation.

Because of the similarity of its signals to those from a moiré-fringe system, the laser interferometer can be used in a very similar way in fully or partially automatic devices. Numerically controlled machine tools and measuring machines are the obvious examples. In a measuring machine constructed at the National Physical Laboratory, scales of various kinds up to a yard in length are checked semi-automatically.[60] A photo-electric microscope detects the calibrations on the moving scale and triggers the counting elements in a programmed manner. In this machine the interferometer signals are sub-divided to provide a finer scale, so as to give a measuring discrimination better than one micro-inch.

Difference frequency methods

The great potential of the laser in communications is due to its mono-chromatic coherent emission which, apart from having a much higher frequency, closely resembles the carrier wave used in normal

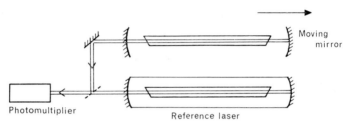

Figure 62 Measurement of small movements by the change in laser frequency.

radio transmission (see Chapter 2). The similarity of laser light to radio waves is such that some of the techniques commonly used at radio frequencies may now be used also at optical frequencies. In particular it is possible to mix the beams of light from two lasers so as to observe a signal at their difference frequency. The beams are simply superposed with a semi-reflector and directed on to a photo-detector. The process is essentially the same as in a moving interferometer, except that now the two beams are derived from different sources.

This principle may be used for measurement because one factor which determines the optical frequency of a laser is the length of its resonant cavity. The optical frequency is broadly determined by the energy levels of the transition involved, but this still allows a variation of perhaps 1000 Mc/s. The precise frequency of operation within this range is set by the mirror separation of the cavity. The laser always adjusts its frequency so that a complete journey round the cavity is an exact number of wavelengths. Thus if one of the cavity mirrors is moved, its movement can be measured from the resulting change of laser frequency, by comparison with a stable reference laser.

For measuring changes of length this method, illustrated in Fig. 62, has exceptional sensitivity. Consider again a helium-neon laser operating on the red line, with a cavity length of one foot. If the mirror separation is changed by one millionth of an inch, the corresponding change of frequency is 40 Mc/s. Since difference frequencies as small as a few cycles per second are detectable, it should in principle be possible to detect movements as small as 10^{-12} inches.

In practice, of course, such sensitivity is seldom necessary — and indeed would be difficult to use. Mechanical vibration would be troublesome, and there might also be confusion because of instability of the reference laser. Nevertheless the sensitivity which can be

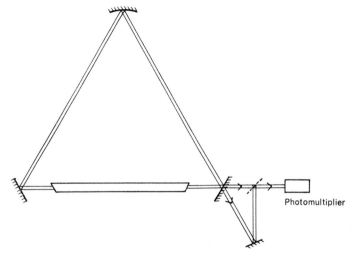

Figure 63   Ring laser, for measurement of rotation.

realized in practice is very high, and by frequency stabilization the drift of a reference laser can be reduced to less than ± 5 Mc/s in a day (corresponding to a zero drift of a tenth of a micro-inch).

Although the difference frequency method can be used to measure movements having a range of many inches, its most likely application is for movements of less than a half-wavelength. There need then be no ambiguity resulting from a change of mode number. One application which has been suggested is for the measurement of distortion in a rock formation due to earth movements. In this case the frequencies of a number of lasers in different orientations, with their mirrors attached to the rock, would be intercompared so that the thermal expansion, affecting all the lasers similarly, would cancel out.

There are naturally many possible uses involving small movements, such as refractive index measurements (with a sample cell in the cavity), small expansions, and so forth. It remains to be seen in which of these applications the technique will prove to be advantageous.

The ring laser

In the ring laser the optical cavity is composed not just of two mirrors between which the light is reflected backwards and forwards, but of three or more mirrors. The light is reflected from one to another, forming a closed loop. Light may propagate round this loop in

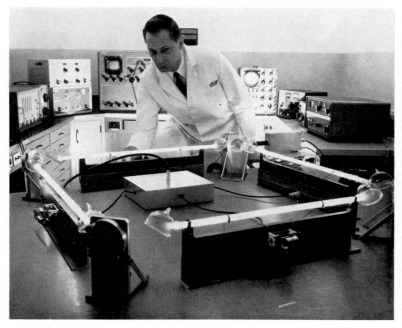

Figure 64 Ring laser experiments in the laboratories of Sperry Gyroscope Company, USA.

either a clockwise or an anticlockwise direction. Whilst the mirror system is stationary both paths are similar, but any rotation of the system causes one optical path to lengthen and the other to shorten. This means that the light beams going round the system in opposite directions have different effective cavity lengths and hence choose slightly different optical frequencies. Their difference frequency may be detected as before, by mixing the beams on a photo-detector, as in Fig. 63. An early ring laser is shown in Fig. 64, and a recent 'solid-state' ring laser in Fig. 65.

A similar kind of optical ring was used to measure rotation by

Sagnac in 1913,[61] and by Michelson and Gale in 1925.[62] The latter experiment was designed to observe the rotation of the earth. The optical ring they used had a circumference of more than a mile, but even then the change of optical path gave only a small effect. The path change was detected by interferometry, the observed fringe shift being approximately a quarter of a fringe.

Figure 65   Recent refinement of the ring laser, developed by Honeywell for the US Navy. This 'solid-state' laser gyroscope has three ring lasers (illuminated), each a block of quartz through which contra-rotating laser beams circulate, as sketched in Figure 63.

The ring laser is much more sensitive because it uses the difference frequency method instead of direct interferometry. The output frequency is given by $f = \dfrac{4\omega A}{\lambda P}$ where A is the area enclosed by the optical path of perimeter P, ω is the rate of angular rotation and λ the wavelength of the light. Thus a triangular path with sides of one foot give a signal of 5 kc/s for a rotation rate of one degree per second.

The ring measures rotation with respect to inertial space — the 'fixed stars' — so that it has potential application for navigation systems, in which it would replace the gyroscope. It has the advantage of having no moving mechanical parts and its digital output is convenient for data analysing systems. At the same time as measuring rates of rotation the ring laser also measures the angle through which it is rotated. Instead of considering the frequency, one must instead count the total number of cycles in the output signal. It is rather like the linear laser interferometer in which counting the number of pulses gives length, whilst the pulse rate (frequency) gives the velocity of the movement. For the 1 ft triangular ring there would be 5000 counts for a rotation of one degree.

Another use of the ring laser is for velocity measurement in a gas or liquid. If in one arm of the ring the light passes through a medium moving in the direction of the light path, then the clockwise and anticlockwise paths will again become unequal, and there will be an output signal.

One of the difficulties which has hindered the immediate application of the ring laser is the tendency for the signal to disappear at low rates of rotation. This usually occurs at a frequency below 1 kc/s and is caused by slight coupling between the clockwise and anticlockwise beams which makes them 'pull-in' to the same frequency. The light scattered from imperfections on the mirror surfaces is apparently sufficient to cause this coupling. Nevertheless the ring laser can be made to operate at low rotation rates if a bias is applied which causes a difference between the optical lengths of the clockwise and anticlockwise paths. A promising method of doing this is by means of the Faraday effect.

Ranging with the laser

Doped crystal and semiconductor lasers cannot at present match the gas laser for spectral purity of output. Nevertheless they too have application in length measurement. The Q-switched solid-state laser emits an extremely bright flash of light with a very short pulse width. Whereas the helium-neon gas laser may emit perhaps 10 milliwatts continuously, a Q-switched ruby laser can emit 10 megawatts during a pulse lasting 20 nanoseconds. The very high power of this flash enables it to be transmitted over comparatively long distances before the atmospheric absorption makes it too weak to be detected. Indeed, the power is sufficient to give an adequate return signal from a diffusely reflecting target, even at a range of several miles in daylight.

In the laser range-finder the time taken for the light to travel to the target and back is measured (see also Chapter 9). The distance is then calculated from a knowledge of the velocity of light under the ambient conditions. In practice, the time is measured by an electronic counter, which counts from a crystal oscillator of such frequency that each count represents a convenient length unit.

The accuracy of the rangefinder is limited mainly by the uncertainty in timing the returned pulse, which depends upon the duration and rise time of the laser pulse. An error of 10^{-8} seconds, for example, would correspond to a distance of 5 feet. The maximum distance which can be measured is governed by the absorption of the atmosphere and the reflectivity of the target. For a normal diffuse target a daylight range of at least 7 miles can be expected under conditions of average visibility. With an appropriate reflector system on the target the range should be considerably increased, as it is also for ranging on targets outside the Earth's atmosphere.

The important feature of the laser range-finder is that the measurement is so quick and easy. It can be operated by one person to measure the range of anything within sight, even a moving target, and the result is presented immediately and unambiguously. The military application seems assured (Chapter 6), but it is not certain to what extent it will be used for other purposes. For most surveying applications the precision will have to be improved and there is unfortunately a health hazard in that the emitted beam is powerful enough to cause permanent eye damage if viewed, even from a considerable range. This hazard is discussed by Desmond Smart in Chapter 8.

The semiconductor laser can be used in a pulsed manner in a range-finder system similar to that described above for the Q-switched crystal or glass laser. The pulse power is however much less, so that the maximum range is restricted at the moment to something of the order of a mile. The compensating advantages are that the semiconductor laser is much more efficient, can be used with a much higher repetition rate, and is physically smaller. The high overall efficiency of approximately 20 per cent in the conversion of electric current into light is, however, only achieved at the present time when the laser is cooled to liquid nitrogen temperatures (77°K). This is a disadvantage in portable equipment, although the 'mini-cooler' working from compressed nitrogen gas avoids the necessity of transporting liquid nitrogen.

Other laser instruments

The techniques which have been described are those which the development of the laser has brought into particular prominence. There are probably many other ways in which the properties of laser radiation will be used in measurement. As the various kinds of laser become more and more developed, they will undoubtedly tend to replace the other light sources at present used in optical instruments.

For example, in the Geodimeter a high-pressure mercury arc is modulated at a radio frequency by means of a Kerr cell. This instrument is used for surveying, having an error of less than half an inch at short ranges and one or two parts in a million at longer ranges (up to 30 miles at night). A coherent source would perhaps be advantageous in this kind of instrument in that the directional output of a laser could improve the effective source efficiency.

Similarly the laser has possibilities for the Mekometer. The Mekometer uses radio-frequency modulation of a pulsed light source for measurements up to a range of about one mile, with an accuracy of three parts in a million (or 1 mm at short distances). Here again a semiconductor or gas laser source may replace the xenon flash tube to improve the source brightness and its electrical efficiency. Indeed there are probably many optical devices which can benefit from a laser source to give a useful, if unspectacular, improvement of performance or efficiency.

It is reasonable to expect that with their continued development, lasers may eventually replace discharge tube sources in many instruments, just as transistors are replacing valves in electronic equipment.

11

TRENDS IN LASER DEVELOPMENT

PROFESSOR O. S. HEAVENS
University of York

It is a fairly straightforward matter to discuss the present trends of laser development, although a much more difficult one to deal with likely future trends. At the time of writing, the performances of many standard laser systems are at a level which would have been dismissed as totally unrealistic in the first year or two of the laser's life span. In some ways this is a strange thing, since much of what has been achieved was predictable at an early stage. The predictions, however, appeared at the time so staggering that one was distrustful, perhaps allowing emotion to cloud one's paper-and-pen reasonings.

At this time we may distinguish four general classes of laser, as follows:

1. Optically excited gas systems.
2. Electronically excited gas systems.
3. Doped-crystal systems.
4. Semiconductor systems.

The first three were discussed in Chapter 3, the fourth type in Chapter 4.

Optically excited gas systems

Progress in the last three of this group has been continuous and rapid. The first-mentioned includes the system originally proposed by Schawlow and Townes (Chapter 1), which had the virtue of simplicity, at least in concept. Atoms of metal vapour are to be illuminated with monochromatic radiation of a suitable wavelength, causing the atoms to be raised to a specific excited level. From here they relax to the ground state via an intermediate level. Suitable choice of material and energy levels yields a system in which the intermediate level empties more rapidly than the upper one, which is a necessary condition for population inversion.

In the system first proposed, potassium vapour was to be the active medium, irradiated with light from a mercury lamp. The necessary properties of the system were well documented. There was only one snag — the system did not work. This was a classic case of 'reliable' theory and 'reliable' experiment disagreeing violently, by large factors. At a later stage, an essentially similar system, employing caesium vapour and a helium lamp, was successfully operated, giving laser emissions in the infrared, at 3 and 7 microns. The reasons for the failure of the potassium system are still not understood.

It seems unlikely at this stage that systems of this type will be further developed. Although the system has the advantage that one excited level is filled specifically, the need for a sharp spectral line at *exactly* the right wavelength is a severe restriction. The caesium laser represented a *tour de force* — hideous experimental problems, consequent upon trying to mix precision optics with hot, reactive caesium vapour, had to be overcome.

Electronically excited gas systems

In the second class of lasers, in which excitation to upper states is effected by electron collision excitation, the development has been most interesting. The first system, arrived at by Javan and his co-workers at Bell Telephone Laboratories (Chapter 1), was developed in a superbly co-ordinated, systematic piece of research in which each stage was thoroughly explored and understood before the next step was taken. In this way, the mode of operation of the helium-neon laser was pretty thoroughly understood by the time the laser first operated.

Further research of this kind followed, but this now appears to have given place to a cut-and-try approach which — astonishingly, when compared with the early development — seems to be enormously successful as a means of building new lasers. From present evidence one can with sublime confidence predict that if one puts some gas (any gas) in a tube at a pressure of, say, tens of torrs (give or take an order of magnitude), the whole placed between suitable reflectors, then on passing a current — preferably a big one — oscillation will occur, probably on several lines at once. In the unlikely event of failure, make the tube bigger. If it still does not work, increase the current. As a last resort, pulse it.

Recent developments of this kind, using the rare gases (as described in Chapter 3) have led to lasers giving continuous operation with powers of the order of hundreds of watts in single lines — an increase of some five orders of magnitude over the original helium-neon system. With the occurrence of simultaneous operation of several lines, the prospect is good for a 'white' light source, which, however, would be white only in the subjective sense. The usual white light source is thermal and emits its energy over a continuous band of wavelengths. The 'white' laser source would be a multi-line source, rather like the usual mercury discharge source, but with enormously greater brightness.

The efficiency of many gas lasers of this type is at present low. For most systems, the efficiency is less than 1 per cent, although the carbon dioxide laser has operated at efficiencies of 10–20 per cent. There are difficulties associated with the very high current densities which are necessary to produce high powers — failure of the containing tube, and erosion of the cathodes through heavy ion bombardment are typical troubles. The use of more highly refractory materials (such as sapphire) for the gas tubes is likely to improve matters. Detailed understanding of the mechanism of operation of many systems of this type is at present lacking and it is likely that, when the necessary studies of this emission spectra and of the electronic conditions in the tube are completed, high efficiencies will result.

Doped-crystal lasers

In the realm of solid-state, doped-crystal lasers, the story is a very different one. In general, careful studies of the absorption and fluorescent spectra of likely materials have preceded their successful operation as lasers.

Ruby has by now been rather completely dealt with and still remains one of the highest-power materials available. The present limitations centre on the shortcomings in optical perfection of the crystal used. Most large rubies are grown by the Verneuil method, in which close control of growth conditions is not easy. The optical quality of crystals grown by the flux-melt method, in which the sapphire and chromium oxide are dissolved in a flux such as lead fluoride, is significantly better than that of Verneuil-grown crystals but it has not so far proved possible to grow very large crystals in this way.

The greater ease with which glass of high optical quality may be made has resulted in the rapid growth of the neodymium-glass laser. This material, like ruby, is capable of operating at very high power levels (although the most powerful systems delivered to date do in fact use ruby rods). Since neodymium-glass operates as a four-level system, the threshold for laser action is lower than that for ruby. For some purposes, the fact that the emission is in the infrared is a disadvantage, although green light may be produced by second harmonic generation — an aspect to which I shall return.

One difficulty with high-power systems is the fact that, during the laser's operation, distortion of the crystal occurs, due to heating. The latter results from the fact that the usual sources of pumping radiation give out energy in wavelength regions which are absorbed by the laser crystal, although without necessarily contributing to the laser oscillation energy. Also, even when radiation confined to the best wavelength range for producing laser action is absorbed, a fraction of this energy is taken up by the crystal lattice as heat. There is no easy way of avoiding this problem although a subtle variation in distribution of 'dope' atoms may help. At the present time this approach is outside the scope of crystal-growing techniques.

Apart from ruby and neodymium-glass, large numbers of doped crystals have been successfully used as lasers. These have generally employed rare-earth, transition metal or actinide series elements in a variety of host lattices. We are beginning to understand in some detail the factors which determine whether a given lattice will form a suitable host for a dope material. As yet only a modest number of combinations of host and dope have been exploited, often because of difficulties in growing crystals of adequate quality.

One of the more exciting current developments in the doped-crystal field is that in which dope atoms of more than one type are employed. It may happen that dope 'A' is good at absorbing radiation from the pumping lamp but does not provide suitable laser transitions, whereas dope 'B' is a good laser line source but with insufficient absorption bands for pumping. In this case it may be possible to absorb pump radiation through atom 'A' and to transfer some of the excitation energy to atom 'B'. In some circumstances ion 'A' may transfer practically the whole of its excitation energy to 'B', by the process of resonant transfer discussed in Chapter 3, and so produce a high density of excited 'B' ions, which then contribute to the laser emission.

The details of this process may be followed by studying the spectral lines emitted by the 'A' + 'B' doped solid during the period immediately following a flash of excitation. The emission from the different ions is characterized by the emitted wavelength and one can follow the transfer of energy from one ion to another. Much remains to be learned of the precise mechanism by which the energy transfer occurs.

At this stage, the power levels at which doped crystal systems operate is, with the exception of ruby and neodymium-glass, fairly low. It is likely however that, as a deeper understanding of such transfer processes is obtained, high performance, together with a wide range of laser emission wavelengths, will be attained. Of special importance in this type of system is that of exciting the laser crystals by means of solar radiation since this provides a simple, direct means of operating lasers — for example, for communication purposes — in space vehicles. Present systems involving yttrium aluminium garnet achieve outputs of the order of a watt and may reasonably be expected to produce 10–100 times this power in due course.

Many of the processes involved in laser action in doped crystals entail the exchange of energy between dope atoms and the lattice vibrations of the host crystal. In many cases, our information on the lattice vibrations — which cover a wide frequency range — of crystal materials is extremely limited. The frequencies at which we need information about lattice waves often fall in a rather difficult region for experimental purposes. On the theoretical side, the problems are so difficult and necessitate such severe simplifications that accurate numerical results cannot be expected. It is likely that there will be an interesting two-way traffic of progress between the laser and lattice-wave fields. Advances in our knowledge of lattice vibrations is likely to speed up the development of lasers; and the laser offers a useful experimental tool (in which lattice waves can be generated, for example, by the use of two laser beams simultaneously) for work on lattice vibrations.

Semiconductor lasers

These systems occupy a special place in the laser family, differing markedly in their mode of excitation from other solid-state systems and gas systems. Not only do they require nothing more than a d.c. supply (although supplemented by cooling facilities if high-power operation is to be achieved), but their output may be modulated directly by modulation of the exciting current.

At the present stage of development, the quality and stability of their radiative output falls far short of those of other systems. Emission linewidths are typically in the region of 10-100 angstroms for oscillation wavelengths around 9000 angstroms, a ratio of the order 1:500. This may be contrasted with the figure of a 1:200,000 for typical doped-crystal lasers and with a 1:10^{14} for highly stabilized gas lasers.

At present, the emission from semiconductor diodes is from a very thin transition layer, only microns deep, between the n and p regions of the semiconductor, resulting in a beam which, although narrow in one dimension, diverges considerably in the perpendicular direction. This is because of the reflecting surfaces constituting the resonator are perpendicular to the plane of the junction region. If sufficient gain can be obtained, it would seem reasonable to arrange the reflecting surfaces to be *parallel* to the junction, thus producing a larger emitting area and a more tightly confined beam. Operation in this fashion has in fact been achieved in one system.

Present efforts with semiconductor lasers include searches for new materials with a view to extending the range of wavelengths emitted, which now is from 0.7 to 8.5 microns. The absence of materials with a sufficiently large band-gap is likely to limit the extension of the range on the short-wave side.

Other laser systems — actual or possible

Fairly early in the development of lasers the tantalizing notion of using organic liquids or glasses as active media was proposed. The ones of particular interest are those with a rare-earth ion sitting in a fairly elaborate molecule; encaged, as it were, so that the immediate neighbourhood of the active ion is shielded from the effects of the motion of, for example, the surrounding solute molecules.

The use of a liquid system is attractive from the high-power operation angle — flow the active material through the resonator and on to a heat-exchanger. The use of organic structures suggests the possibility of adjusting the laser emission frequency by suitable design of the surrounding molecular architecture. Lasers of this type have been successfully operated — one uses europium dibenzl methide — although there are several difficulties which severely limit their performance. The absorption coefficient of the chelates so far examined is very high, giving use to pumping problems, and the viscosity of these materials is so high that the circulating notion is not feasible. Most present systems work only at rather low temperatures (around 150°C), although some materials are capable of low-power operation at room temperature. The present outlook for materials of this type does not appear highly promising, although the number and range of types of systems investigated so far are small.

A possible approach to obtaining the inverted population necessary for laser action is that of using a suitable exothermic chemical reaction. In many such processes (flames, for instance) a substantial concentration of excited atoms is formed, in excited states. Thus when atomic hydrogen and chlorine combine a substantial amount of energy is released and the hydrogen chloride forms in an excited state. Although most of the excitation energy serves to produce high rotational energy of the molecule, it is thought that sufficient should go into vibrational energy to give a usable inversion. The concentration of excited atoms depends on two factors: first, how fast excited atoms are being produced by the chemical reaction; and secondly, how rapidly they decay. With plausible numbers for known chemical reactions and molecular decay rates, it appears that a medium with sufficient inversion to give large gain could be produced.

No such system exists at this time. The problems of getting an optically stable region of gas which is being produced from something like an oxy-acetylene burner are severe indeed. The nearest to chemical lasers so far operated are those in which an inverted population is produced by *dissociation* of molecules. Thus carbon monoxide, oxygen and nitrogen are used, mixed with rare-gas atoms in a discharge tube. Electrons excite the rare gas atoms to metastable levels which then collide with the carbon monoxide, oxygen or other molecules, dissociate them, and produce suitable concentrations of excited atoms or ions. Dr Goodwin discusses such systems in Chapter 3.

One of the dramatic developments in laser research has been the suddenly acquired facility to investigate non-linear optical effects. It has always been possible to write, formally, that the polarization P of a solid depends on applied electric field E, according to a relation such as $P = E + aE^2 + bE^3 + \ldots$. It had never before been possible to produce light beams where E was big enough for the E^2 and E^3 effects to be detectable. So we have been left with $P = E$, which simply tells us that if we put a sine-wave E_0 sin ωt (for example, a light wave of frequency ω) into a crystal, the resultant polarization would also have a frequency ω. Nothing odd would be expected.

When, however, we put an intense enough E in, we have the polarization taking the form $P = E_0$ sin $\omega t + aE_0^2$ $\sin^2 \omega t$ which can be written instead as $P = A + B$ sin $\omega t + C$ sin $2\omega t$. This shows that the molecules in the solid change their state of polarization at twice the frequency of the excited light. We can think of the molecules as tiny aerials, radiating signals. We thus expect the solid under this condition to give out light of double the frequency, and this is precisely what is observed. When infrared radiation from a neodymium-glass laser is focused in a suitable crystal, such as triglycine sulphate, or ammonium dihydrogen phosphate, green light of wavelength just one half of the 1.064 microns of the exciting light streams out.

The generation of harmonics in this way is of interest as a method of studying solids and also as a means of producing quite large amounts of second harmonic radiation — efficiencies of up to some 25 per cent have been reported. The high fields needed tend to cause damage in the crystal used, although this may often be due to imperfections. Renewed effort at the crystal-growing end may produce improvement here, as in the case of the laser crystals themselves.

When very high intensity beams of light are focused on crystals, as in the last-mentioned system, fracture sometimes occurs, arising from the very intense sound waves produced in the crystal as a result of electro-striction — the change in dimensions of a crystal with electrical field. In fact we see one aspect of a probable development in which lasers will be used as a powerful means of studying lattice vibrations in crystals. In this way, information will be obtained, indirectly through the optical-acoustical scattering processes involved, about lattice vibration frequencies which are at present quite inaccessible to normal methods of experiment.

Yet another field which the laser shows signs of transforming is that concerned with Raman scattering. In this process, a radiation quantum is absorbed by a molecule and a small amount of energy is taken up, after which the molecule re-emits radiation — now at a slightly lower frequency. Alternatively, a small addition of energy may occur, and radiation of higher frequency be emitted. In either case, the *difference* between the absorbed and emitted frequencies is a

149

characteristic of the molecule. From detailed studies, information about the molecule may be obtained.

This, the Raman effect, is not itself new. The intensity of the Raman scattered lines is, however, extremely low and has hitherto required very high pressure lamps and very long exposures. The high pressure lamps produce such broad emission lines that Raman lines near the exciting frequency are completely obscured. The laser — as the only light source in which the line width gets *smaller* as the power increases — is ideal for this purpose. By including Raman-active materials in the laser cavity, many Raman lines build up in intensity in a fashion generally similar to that of the 'primary' laser line, giving rise to stimulated Raman emission.

The study of the wide variety of Raman effects precipitated by the use of lasers requires considerable effort before a complete understanding is reached. It may well be that the new field created by this laser application will be as important for future spectroscopists as the field of conventional spectroscopy has been since its inception.

Whither lasers?

The 'feet' of this chapter have been kept reasonably close to the ground. It would be rather easy to allow one's imagination to ramble on with hypothetical changes of yet more orders of magnitude in the various quantities involved. Indeed, this hardly seems necessary since it is unlikely that we yet appreciate fully the significance and potentialities of the lasers which we already possess.

When the available linewidth of optical sources shrinks by seven orders of magnitude almost overnight, one pauses for breath. It hardly seemed fruitful — even ten years ago — to speculate on the few cycles per second line broadening of a Rayleigh-scattered beam of radiation when one could not do better than produce lines many millions of cycles in width. Why bother about discussing the high order terms in expressions for permittivity, when one was, in the optical region, 'inescapably' confined to linear regions?

One's tendency is, naturally enough, to be looking at the things one could do with just a further two or three orders of magnitude in sensitivity. The change in orders of magnitude of the quantities connected with laser beams — power, linewidth, energy/unit bandwidth — is so enormous that one is caught out. One can look to a period during which the vast field, particularly of fundamental studies of matter — atomic and molecular, in solid and liquid state — will be explored with this new tool.

At the same time the laser itself will further develop, both in the region of high pulse powers (10^{12} watts with a pulse duration of 10^{-11} second should be possible according to Townes) in the proliferation of high-power continuous wave systems and in low power systems with more subtle forms of control. At the present time systems with radically different modes of operation from those discussed above do not appear as likely competitors. The scene could be transformed by unexpected developments, but this takes us to the realm of the crystal ball.

REFERENCES

1. Gordon J. P., Zeiger H. J., Townes C. H., *Physical Review*, Vol. 95, p. 282, 1954.
2. Townes C. H. and Schawlow A., *Physical Review*, Vol. 112, p. 1940, 1958.
3. Cutler C. C., *International Science and Technology*, No. 21, p.54, 1963.
4. Rigden J. D. and Gordon E. I., *Proc. IRE*, p. 2367, Nov. 1962.
5. Oliver B. M., *Proc. IEEE*, p. 220, Jan. 1963.
6. Allen L. and Jones D. G. C., *Physics Letters* Vol. 7, p. 321, 1963.
7. Eaglesfield C. C. *New Scientist*, Vol. 22, p. 498, 1964.
8. Gabor D., *Proc. Roy. Soc.* (A), Vol. 197, p. 454, 1949.
9. Leith E. N. and Upatnieks J., *J.Opt.Soc.Am.*, Vol. 54, p. 1295, 1964.
10. Gabor D., *Holography, or the 'whole picture'*, New Scientist, Vol. 29, p. 74, 1966.
11. Maiman T. H., *Physical Review*, Vol. 123, p. 1145, 1961.
12. Javan A., Bennett W. R., and Herriott D. R., *Physical Review Letters*, Vol. 6, p. 106, 1961.
13. Rom-Kvicherskaya I. A., Ratner A. M., and Meshchoryakav A. V., *Optics and Spectroscopy*, Vol. 19, p. 264, 1965.
14. Kiss Z. J., and Duncan R. C., *Applied Physics Letters*, Vol. 5, p. 200, 1964.
15. Bridges W. B., *Applied Physics Letters*, Vol. 4, p. 128, 1964.
16. Patel C. K. N., *Physical Review Letters*, Vol. 13, p. 617, 1964.
17. McFarlane R. A., Patel C. K. N., and Bennett W. R., *Proc. IRE* Vol. 50, p. 2111, 1962.
18. White A. D. and Rigden J. D., *Proc. IRE*, Vol. 50, p. 2366, 1962.
19. Gordon E. I., Labude E. F., and Bridges W. B., *Applied Physics. Letters*, Vol. 4, p. 178, 1964.
20. Bennett W. R., Knutson J. W., Mercer G. N., and Detch J. L., *Applied Physics Letters*, Vol. 4, p. 180, 1964.
21. Patel C. K. N., *Physical Review*, Vol. 136, p. 1187, 1964.

22. Patel C. K. N., *Applied Physics Letters*, Vol. 7, p. 15, 1965.
23. Nasledov D. N. *et al*, *Soviet Physics — Solid State*, Vol. 4, p. 782, 1962.
24. Hall R. N. *et al*, *Physical Review Letters*, Vol. 9, p. 366, 1962.
25. Nathan M. I. *et al*, *Applied Physics Letters*, Vol. 1, p. 62, 1962.
26. Rediker R. H., *Physics Today*, Vol. 18, p. 42, 1965.
27. Basov N. G., Bogdankevitch O. V., Devyatkov A. G., *Proc. Symposium on Radiative Recombination in Semiconductors*, Paris 1964, p. 225.
28. Born M. and Wolf E., *Principles of Optics* (2nd ed.,), Pergamon, 1964.
29. Leith E. N. and Upatnieks J., *J.Opt.Soc.Am.*, Vol. 53, p. 1377. 1963.
30. Stroke G. W. *et al*, *Nature*, Vol. 209, p. 603, 1966.
31. Stroke G. W. *et al*, *Nature*, Vol. 208, p. 1159, 1965.
32. Gabor D. *Nature*, Vol. 208, p. 422, 1965.
33. Miller B., *Optical systems have space potential*, *Aviation Week*, 14th December, p. 87, 1959.
34. Thirring H., *The myth of laser 'death rays'*, *New Scientist*, Vol. 18, p. 595, 1963.
35. Miller B., *US begins laser weapons programs*, *Aviation Week and Space Technology*, 26th March, p. 41, 1962.
36. Klass P. J., *US increases radiation weapons studies*, *Aviatoni Week and Space Technology*, 4th December, p. 52, 1961.
37. Anon, *Laser research gains*, *Aviation Week and Space Technology*, 28th June, p. 98, 1965.
38. Anon., *Tactical laser*, *Soviet Science in the News*, Vol. 3, No. 2, July, 1965.
39. Remarks by Major General John G. Zierdt, Commanding General, US Army Missile Command at Department of Defense Advanced Planning Briefings for Industry, Los Angeles, California, 4th March, 1965.
40. Miller B., *Fire control system applies laser radar*, *Aviation Week and Space Technology*, 17th August, p. 69, 1964.
41. Private communication, Jack L. Jenkins, formerly manager, Aircraft Tactical Systems, Hughes Aircraft.
42. Miller B., *Air Reconnaissance aided by line-scanning laser camera*, *Aviation Week and Space Technology*, 26th April, p. 81, 1965.
43. Townes C. H., *IEEE Spectrum*, Vol. 2, p. 30, 1965.
44. Fairbanks R. H. and Adams C. M., *Welding Journal Research Supplement*, March 1964.
45. Steigerwald K. H., US Patent 2,793,281.
46. Leonard D. A., *Applied Physics Letters*, Vol. 7, p. 4, 1965.
47. Kaplan R. A., National Electronics Conference, October, 1964.

48. Anderson J. E. and Jackson J. E., Spring Meeting of the Optical Society of America, 1965.
49. *Laser Newsletter*, No. 15, March 1965.
50. Ready J. F., *Journal of Applied Physics*, Vol. 36, p. 462, 1965.
51. Honig R. E. and Woolston J. R., *Applied Physics Letters*, Vol. 2, p. 138, 1963.
52. Archbold E., Harper D. W. and Hughes T. P., *British Journal of Applied Physics*, Vol. 12, p. 1321, 1964.
53. Ehler A. W., *Bull.Am.Phys.Soc.*, Vol. 10, p. 227, 1965.
54. Tozer B. A., Smy P. R. and Wright J. K., *Proc.Phys.Soc.*, Vol. 86, p. 45, 1965.
55. Boyd W., *Pathology*, pub. Henry Kimpton.
56. *The Essentials of Histology*, Schaeffer, pub. Witman.
57. *Applied Physiology*, Samson Wright, pub. Keele and Neil.
58. Ashby D. E. T. F., Jephcott D. F., Malein A. and Raynor F. A., *Journal of Applied Physics*, Vol. 36, p. 29, 1965.
59. Peck E. R. and Obetz S. W., *J.Opt.Soc.Am.*, Vol. 43, p. 505, 1953.
60. Rowley W. R. C. and Stanley V. W., *Machinery* (Lond.), Vol. 107, p. 780, 1965.
61. Sagnac M. G., *Comptes Rendus*, Vol. 157, p. 708, 1913; and *Journal de Physique*, Vol. 4, p. 177, 1914.
62. Michelson A. A. and Gale H. C., *Nature*, Vol. 115, p. 566, 1925; and *Astrophysical Journal*, Vol. 61, p. 140, 1925.

THE AUTHORS

John Howard Sanders (*The birth of the laser*) is Fellow and Tutor in Physics in Oriel College, Oxford, and a University Lecturer in Physics. He also carries out laser research. In 1959 he spent several months at the Bell Telephone Laboratories. Dr Sanders obtained his doctorate in Oxford, where he was Senior Proctor from 1962–63. He is forty-two, married with three daughters and one son, and enjoys tennis, fishing and gardening in his spare time. He has published *The Fundamental Atomic Constants* and *The Velocity of Light*.

Charles Cecil Eaglesfield (*The nature of laser light*) works at the Standard Telecommunication Laboratories, Harlow, Essex, where he is concerned with the possibilities of communication at optical wavelengths. He has been in the electronics field for many years. His activities include work done during the early days of television and radar. He was educated at Peterhouse, Cambridge. Mr Eaglesfield is sixty, married, with one daughter; he lives in Harlow. He has published *Laser Light*.

Dennis Gabor (*Holography by laser light*) is Professor of Applied Electron Physics at the Imperial College of Science and Technology, London. Born in Hungary, he was educated at the Technical University, Budapest, and at the Technische Hochschule, Berlin-Charlottenburg. Professor Gabor, a prolific inventor, is sixty-five. He was a research engineer with the German firm, Siemens and Halske, and later with the (then) British Thomson-Houston Company in Rugby. Professor Gabor was elected into the Royal Society in 1956. He is author of *Inventing the Future*.

Deryck William Goodwin (*Solid-state and gas lasers*) is a Principal Scientific Officer at the Ministry of Aviation's Royal Radar Establishment, Malvern. He leads a large section working on solid-state lasers, their physics and their applications. Dr Goodwin was educated at Lincoln School and Birmingham University, where he gained his Ph.D. He is thirty-eight, unmarried, and lives in Malvern, enjoying music, artistic lighting (he designed the lighting for Lincoln Cathedral) and swimming in his free time.

Cyril Hilsum (*Semiconductor lasers*) is a Senior Principal Scientific Officer at the Ministry of Aviation's Royal Radar Establishment at Malvern, where he works with semiconducting compounds. Previously, he was with the Services Electronics Research Laboratory at Baldock where, in 1962, he made the first British semiconducting laser. He gained his Ph.D. in London University. Dr Hilsum is forty-one, married with two daughters, and lives in Malvern. He is co-author of *Semiconducting III-V Compounds*.

Barry Miller (*The laser on the battlefield*) was, until recently, Avionics Editor of *Aviation Week and Space Technology*, for which he worked for the past seven years. His first of more than a score of articles on lasers, discussing their possible military applications, appeared in 1959 — before the laser had been invented. Mr Miller gained his degree in electrical engineering from the Brooklyn Polytechnic Institute, and studied liberal arts at the University of Chicago and the New School for Research, New York. He is thirty-seven, married with two children, and lives in Los Angeles. He was invited to read a paper on 'Line scanning laser reconnaissance' at a New York Academy of Sciences conference in 1965. Mr Miller has now joined an investment company.

Kenneth Firth (*The laser as a source of heat*) is a Senior Scientist, in charge of the Laser Applications Group at Associated Electrical Industries' Central Research Laboratory, Rugby. From 1948–63 he worked at AEI's Aldermaston Research Laboratory as a physicist. His chief responsibilities are the development of lasers and their applications, and work on holography. Dr Firth gained his Ph.D. from Reading University. He is 41, married with two children, and lives in Rugby. He enjoys gardening, and exploring England and Wales.

Desmond Smart (*The laser in medicine*) is Head of the Medical Applications Group at the International Research and Development Company, and Senior Research Associate in the Department of Ophthalmology at the University of Newcastle upon Tyne. Previously he worked for C. A. Parsons, parent company of IRD, from 1956, at first on nuclear research. He holds a Master of Science degree in Physics from King's College, Durham. Mr Smart, who is thirty-three, is married with two sons and lives in Tynemouth. He is a pianist and organist, specializing in Bach, and he also enjoys shooting.

Keith Dillon Harris (*The laser in telecommunications*) is Manager of the Advanced Engineering Laboratory of G. and E. Bradley Limited, South Ruislip, Middlesex. He takes special interest in new devices for communications. Previously he was Head of the Maser Laboratory of Glass Developments Limited. Mr Harris graduated from the Chelsea college of Science and Technology, in London. He is thirty-five, married with four daughters, and lives in the Buckinghamshire village of Iver. He has published a monograph on *Lasers*.

William Richard Charlton Rowley (*The laser in measurement and control*) is a Senior Scientific Officer at the Ministry of Technology's National Physical Laboratory, where is he concerned chiefly with the measurement of length by interferometry, and particularly with developing light sources for primary and secondary wavelength standards. Dr Rowley gained his Ph.D. from King's College, Newcastle. He is thirty-one, unmarried, and lives at Hampton, Middlesex. Music and its high-fidelity reproduction, growing the perfect lawn, and ice skating and ice dancing are his chief leisure interests.

Oliver Samuel Heavens (*Trends in laser development*) is Professor of Physics in the University of York. Previously he was Reader in Physics in the University of London. His research lies chiefly with lasers and with the physics of thin films. Professor Heavens gained his Ph.D. from Reading University and his D.Sc. from London University. He is Chairman of the Optical Group of the Institute of Physics and Physical Society. Professor Heavens is forty-three, married with three children, and lives in York. His leisure pursuits include mountaineering and sailing. He has published *Optical Properties of Thin Films* and *Optical Masers*.

David Fishlock (*Editor*) has been Technology Editor of *New Scientist* for the past four years. He is thirty-four, married with a son, and lives in Chalfont St Giles, Buckinghamshire. He has published several books, the latest (in press) being *The New Materials*, a discussion of the materials of which advanced technology is made.

INDEX